FROM LEICESTER

Edited by Allison Dowse

First published in Great Britain in 2000 by
YOUNG WRITERS
Remus House,
Coltsfoot Drive,
Woodston,
Peterborough, PE2 9JX
Telephone (01733) 890066

HB ISBN 0 75431 902 4
SB ISBN 0 75431 903 2

FOREWORD

This year, the Young Writers' Future Voices competition proudly presents a showcase of the best poetic talent from over 42,000 up-and-coming writers nationwide.

Successful in continuing our aim of promoting writing and creativity in children, our regional anthologies give a vivid insight into the thoughts, emotions and experiences of today's younger generation, displaying their inventive writing in its originality.

The thought, effort, imagination and hard work put into each poem impressed us all and again the task of editing proved challenging due to the quality of entries received, but was nevertheless enjoyable. We hope you are as pleased as we are with the final selection and that you continue to enjoy *Future Voices From Leicester* for many years to come.

CONTENTS

Soar Valley College

The Poems

THE THREE WITCHES

Nasty, nasty spell of the west
I'll make a spell that is the best
Two legs of a bony frog
And two ears of a lazy dog
Four big hairy bats
And two small howling cats
Wool of sheep
Two black dogs sleep
While all the rest will weep and weep
Nasty, nasty spell of the west
I'll make a spell that is the best.

Cherrie Cooper (11)

MY BULLIED CHILD

I take my child to school,
Knowing what's going to happen
to him,
I wave him off
to his class.

The bell rings
and he runs up to me
and when we get home
he tells me what happened
he cries.
I cry.
I tell the teachers about it
but they do
            Nothing.

Aneeka Pathak (13)
Beaumont Leys School

DARK

Dark is when the sun goes down.
Dark is when the lights go out.
Dark is when you lift up a rock.
Dark is the shadow between the boat and its dock.
Dark is a blackboard.
Dark is black paint.
Dark is the mind of a person insane.
Dark is inside a very large hole.
Dark is black, the black of coal.
Dark is unkind.
Dark is grey.
Dark is no more in the month of May.
Dark is a cave, dark is a cave.
Dark is the dance floor of a club or a rave.
Dark is a prison cell.
Dark is dark like the darkness of hell.

Laura Lee (13)
Beaumont Leys School

GRANDMA

(In memory of my grandma. I will never forget you)

I never said goodbye,
But now I sit down and cry.
I hope you rest in peace,
Because that's the way it should be.
When they said you were dead,
I said 'Did she die in her bed?'
I think of you every day,
But really I wish you could stay.
There's not a good thing about this time,
But I tell you now, you'll always be in my mind.

Jenna Wells (12)
Beaumont Leys School

THE ULTIMATE HORROR MONSTER

The ultimate horror monster
enjoys feasting on human skin.
This gruesome, vile thing
lives in the dark, gloomy caverns of Transylvania.

Its table manners need improving
It picks up its food (human) with its blooded claw
and opens its huge, mile-wide jaw
Crack!
Crunch!
Goes the noise of bones crunching and munching.

A fresh stream of blood drips from its
Razor teeth and it staggers into
the dark night leaving traces of blood
and saliva as it returns to its den full of skeletons
after destroying another Transylvanian village.

Aakash Patny (12)
Beaumont Leys School

FLY PIE

My frog lives in a tank
I found him at the river bank.
He was slimy and green
And wasn't too keen
On coming with me
For our evening tea
When I told him we were having pies,
He said, 'I'll come if you make it flies.'

So that's how I got my green slimy frog
Next time I'll tell you how I got my dog!

Becky Ghent (12)
Beaumont Leys School

EXCUSE ME BUT!

Don't pity me,
You silly fool.
I'm just as good
As you will ever be.

I may be poor,
I know I'm homeless.
But I'm just as good
As you will ever be.

I live in doorways
Parks, tips and hostels.
I beg for money,
But not all the time.
My dog is very weak,
Nothing but skin and bones.
I am always hungry,
I never have any food.

I have rags for clothes,
And no shoes on my feet.
But I am just as good,
As you will ever be.

I have some pride
You follow rules.
I am just as good,
As you will ever be.

Don't pity me,
You silly fool,
You may be good,
But I am better than you.

Rusanda Radulovic (13)
Beaumont Leys School

THE LITTLE BOY

Little boy all sad and low
no one to comfort him
nowhere to go.
Scared and worried
his little eyes weep,
tired but determined to find
a place to sleep,
face all dirty against his
white little eyes,
but still determined
to find somewhere dry.
Wet and cold
he wanders around,
nowhere to sit,
no dry ground.
Finds a little blanket
sitting on the floor,
picks it up
wraps it round him
to keep nice and warm.
The rain has stopped
the weather is
just right.
Finds a dry spot
to sleep for
the night.
Sleeping on the street
his little eyes close.
Will he wake up
in the morning?
Nobody knows.

Kelisha Phillips (13)
Beaumont Leys School

FEAR

I lie in my bed on a dark, dark night,
The bedroom door just gave me a fright.
It creaked and banged. It must be the wind,
But what if it's not? I shiver and cringe.
It may be a big monster to gobble me up,
He'll put my blood and bones in a monster cup.

I fear that the monster is in my room,
Or it may be a witch on a long wooden broom,
Or maybe a goblin with a long pointy nose,
And green mouldy warts on the end of his toes.
Whatever it is, it's nearer and nearer,
If only I could see a little clearer.

I could just run to turn on the light.
No, oh no! I hold my quilt tight.
The fear spreads down to my toes,
The churning in my stomach grows and grows,
I pluck up the courage to jump out of bed,
Then suddenly I realise the fear has left my head,
Standing on my rug I'm aware I've been dreaming,
My eyes are wide open because of my screaming.

Kelly Coulton (12)
Beaumont Leys School

I SAW A HORROR MONSTER

I have seen a horror monster
Only in my dreams
The other day he came to town
And used his laser beams.

So I have seen a horror monster
He smelt of cheesy feet
If you were in town that day
You'd know he's horrid to meet.

You should be grateful that
You didn't see this thing
He was very nasty
And his name was Gingy-Ging.

All the silly people
Who read the horror books
Must be very brave
Cos of the way it looks.

Gopi Raja (12)
Beaumont Leys School

SHOPPING

Everyone rushes in,
Trolleys running over anything in sight,
Babies screaming for their mums,
Little toddlers asking 'Can I have?'
'Can I have?'
Checkouts beeping,
Money being exchanged,
Little known to shoppers
They are being watched all the time.
Everyone seems to go shopping at the same time.
Trolleys are kings of the aisles,
Weaving in and out of each other,
People barging into one another,
Trying to get those last minute bargains.
Long queues at the tills.
Staff running about,
People are waiting and daydreaming,
Not worried about losing their place in the queue.
All because they need to get their weekly shop.

Ashley Bassett (13)
Beaumont Leys School

STEPMOMS

I always thought stepmoms were cruel and nasty,
I always looked upon them as
Evil figures from fairy tales.
I always expected stepmoms to favour
Their own children.
I always saw ugly stepmoms, jealous
Of children not their own.
I always felt coldness
In a stepmom's sharp glare.
I always felt like this
Until now.
Now I have
A stepmom.

Hayley Thompson (13)
Beaumont Leys School

WHAT IS A MILLENNIUM?

What is a millennium?
Does anyone know?
Is the millennium 1000 years?
What do we know?
What will the millennium bring?
Will it bring happiness?
Will it bring sadness?
Does anyone really know?
Will more people die?
Will it make more people live?
Do I really know?
Do you really know?
I guess we will just have to wait.

Natasha Warnes (12)
Beaumont Leys School

ALWAYS SMILING BOY

Always smiling boy,
He was never sulking,
Always smiling,
Marshmallow soft body,
Laughing his head off.
Spinning around the playground,
Enjoying the sun,
Having fun,
Always smiling boy,
'Simple' they called him,
But what a perfect life I say,
So much better than mine,
Stress free,
Always smiling boy.

John Grady (13)
Beaumont Leys School

BLACKBEARD THE PIRATE

B lackbeard was an evil soul.
L ife was good for him.
A favourite brew of his was rum and gunpowder.
C apturing and plundering ships was his game.
K ings were in a fix, he was unstoppable.
B urning matches in his hair he wore in battle.
E dward Teach was his name.
A fearsome pirate was he.
R aiding ships with ease he scourged the seas.
D ied on a British battleship did he, his reign came to an end.
   But his legend goes on.

Gareth Cartwright (13)
Beaumont Leys School

IF ONLY . . .

When I look into the mirror
What do I see?
What I see
Is me.

My hair is long
My face is thin
My eyes are blue
My figure trim.

Clothes are fetching
Shoes are high
Skirt is short
I look so fly.

Then . . .

My face fat
My hair short
My eyes are brown
My laugh a snort.

Clothes are old
Shoes are flat
Skirt is knee-length
My hips fat.

When I look into the mirror
What do I see?
What I see is the
Real me.

Samantha Middleton (13)
Beaumont Leys School

ONLY 17

He was only seventeen
When he first took his post,
Just a young boy,
Earning his respect.

He was only seventeen
When he first held a gun,
Just a young boy,
Trying to prove people wrong.

He was only seventeen
When he first stepped in the trench,
Just a young boy,
Doing his duty.

He was only seventeen
When he did his father proud,
Just a young boy,
Fighting for his country.

He was only seventeen
When he first shot a soul,
Just a young boy,
Following his orders.

He was only seventeen
When he first got killed,
Just a young boy,
Who made a mistake.

Stephen Bramley (12)
Beaumont Leys School

I WANTED TO SCREAM

As I walked into my bedroom,
I had finally met my doom.

> A big, juicy spider lay straight ahead,
> Exactly above my four poster bed.

I wanted to scream but I couldn't,
I wanted to cry but I wouldn't.

> But then I froze just standing there,
> I wanted to move but I wouldn't dare.

If only I could turn around,
As long as I don't make a sound.

> I could run out of my room,
> And eventually escape my doom.

But then finally my brother came,
Just as I was feeling lame.

> 'Get rid of that spider!' I cried,
> As it started to crawl to my side.

My brother actually picked it up,
With a piece of paper and a cup.

> And when it finally disappeared,
> Another of my fears appeared!

On my desk, lay 2 wriggly worms,
Carrying of lots of dirt and germs.

> I wanted to scream but I couldn't,
> I wanted to cry but I wouldn't . . .

Anusha Patel (13)
Beaumont Leys School

A DAY AT THE BEACH

The whole beach is packed
People everywhere,
Putting suntan cream on,
Combing out their hair.

The summer sun is blinding,
Sunbathing in this heat,
Walking on this scolding sand,
It really burns your feet.

The lovely smell of barbecues,
Wafting through the air,
People cooking bacon and eggs,
While people stop and stare.

People with their sunbrollies up,
Sitting in the cool shade,
Children playing on the beach,
With their buckets and spades.

Men standing on surfboards,
On waves which are high,
Licking lollies and ice-creams,
Kites flying in the sky.

People with their swimwear on,
Who have a wonderful tan,
They cool themselves off,
By using a paper fan.

It's 8 o'clock and the beach is bare,
Everyone has gone home,
Watching the waves crashing onto the shore,
Now I'm all on my own!

Natalie Gask (13)
Beaumont Leys School

YOU THINK THAT I DON'T NOTICE

You think that I don't notice
When you snigger behind my back
You think that I don't mind it
When your blow hits me full whack.

But it hurts me that you think this
As I'm sitting there close to tears
And you're thinking what your next step is
Now you know my deepest fears.

So yes, I'm scared of spiders
And I'm terrified of heights
What right have you to make me cry
And lure me into fights?

Natalie Howes (13)
Beaumont Leys School

SNOW

The snowflakes all fall through the air,
On to the snow-sheeted ground,
They scatter down in huge balls,
As they fall through the air,
Snow laidens the ears,
In a soft velvet-like sheet,
The snow is like a fluffy powder,
As it spreads on the lawn.
The puddles are frozen from the cold chill,
And look like glass sculptures.
The snow crunches deeply beneath my uninsulated feet,
The cat leaves her paw prints on the sheet of snow.

Nilesh R Patel (13)
Beaumont Leys School

WHEN THE LIGHTS GO OUT

I'm in my cold, lonely bed and the lights are switched off.
The route to my door looks longer than a mile.
My window is open and howling wind makes my curtains fly.
The light from the street lamps makes creepy shadows on the wall.
They get bigger and bigger.

Shuffle, shuffle.
What's that?
Is it a ghost or a zombie coming to get me?
What shall I do? I'm too scared to move.
The shadows are growing teeth; now eyes and hands.
They're getting closer!
Creak, rattle, moan, chatter.
All these sounds I can hear - everywhere,
In my cupboard, under my bed - everywhere.
Shall I hide?
Or am I cornered?

I can hear footsteps coming up the stairs.
It's definitely a zombie,
Not a ghost - they glide.
The footsteps are getting louder,
My door's opening . . .
'Aren't you asleep yet?'
What a relief - it's my dad.
'No,' I answer.
'Well, you'd better go to sleep soon,' he orders.
Then he goes downstairs,
I start to hear those sounds again.
Moaning, rattling, creaking.

The cupboard door opens.
I see a monstrous, hideous . . .

Shailesh Dahya (12)
Beaumont Leys School

WHEN I GO TO BED

When I go to bed,
I close my eyes and hold my ted.
'What's that noise?' I said.
Getting louder and louder,
'Boo!'
I put on the light and looked back up.
'Oh! It's only my brother Fred,
Go away!' I said.

When I go to bed,
I close my eyes and hold my ted.
'What's that noise?' I said.
Getting louder and louder,
'Whoo!'
I put on the light and looked back up.
'Oh! It's only the gentle wind outside.'

When I go to bed,
I close my eyes and hold my ted.
'What's that noise?' I said.
Getting louder and louder.
'Aaagghh . . .'

Vinesh Gopal (12)
Beaumont Leys School

BUTTERFLIES

Butterflies flutter by,
On a summer's day.
They land on a flower
Then down comes a shower
And the butterflies fly away.

Jodie Mulroy (12)
Beaumont Leys School

FEARS

I am scared,
I am frightened,
I will have nightmares,
I am alone in the house,
In my bed.

> Find me a torch.
> Find me a light.

I am scared,
Frightened, alone,
In the house.

> I am scared,
> I am frightened,
> I will have nightmares.
> I am alone in the house,
> Alone in my bed.

Amy Taylor (12)
Beaumont Leys School

DREAMS

My dream is really exciting
Knights are bold and dragons are fighting.

Well I have a dream that's nice and pretty
With butterflies and a bouncing kitty.

My dream is a nightmare dark and dull
With a mean and ferocious big black bull.

My mum and dad now wake me up,
With steaming coffee in a cup.

Daniel Oates (12)
Beaumont Leys School

I AM A ...

I am a cookie
And I live in a jar
I have many friends
And come from afar.

Yes I'm a biscuit
Small and thin
I get here by packet
And now I'm in a tin.

Wherever I go
I leave crumbs behind
I'm beigy-brown
With chewy chunks inside.

Whenever I'm picked
I'm as glad as can be
I get put in a mouth
And eaten with tea.

Neha Murji (12)
Beaumont Leys School

IN MY WARDROBE

In my wardrobe,
You will find,
A pair of socks,
I've left behind.

In my wardrobe,
You will see,
Three books,
And a chimpanzee.

In my wardrobe,
There would be,
A fluttering fly,
And a buzzing bee.

In my wardrobe,
You will find,
A pair of socks,
I've left behind.

Louise Burhm (12)
Beaumont Leys School

CHANGES

I see no changes,
All I see is dangerous faces,
Criminals,
Who disgrace the races.

Still I see no changes,
Can't the world get peace,
Why won't they stop the war,
In the Middle East?

I never saw changes,
Until someone said, 'I have a dream.'
But is it going to come true,
So it might seem.

That man became a famous leader,
Then people said his campaign was just the thing,
But who was he,
Of course, *Martin Luther King!*

Mitesh Kara (14)
Beaumont Leys School

ME AND MY MUM

My mum's kind,
And very sweet.
She makes our house
Look nice and neat.

She's got long blonde hair,
And narrow blue eyes.
She's got a small round face,
And very slim thighs.

She's quite clever,
She goes to college.
She's very bright,
With all her knowledge.

She cooks my dinner,
And tidies my room.
She loves me loads,
That's what I assume.

James Lewis (12)
Beaumont Leys School

THE COLD

The cold is nasty
The cold makes you sneeze
And sometimes it gives you knobbly knees.
The cold makes you shiver
The cold makes you moan
The cold makes you go through Kleenex faster than you know.

Adam Bird (12)
Beaumont Leys School

TRAPPED LOVE

When you're feeling insecure,
When you're sad and unsure,
When you feel nothing's right for you,
When you have no one to turn to,
Just try to be strong and carry on.

Try not to be afraid,
Just try to be brave,
When your stomach's in a knot,
Try not to think about it a lot,
Keep your head up high and don't cry.

Remember it's not the end,
There's always a friend,
To help and always care,
And remember there is always someone there.

Amy Louise Brown (12)
Beaumont Leys School

OUT TO SPACE

Where does the end of this big world go to?
Out to space, well I should think so.

Into the thin air, black, dull and dimness.
Where the stars stand still, sitting helpless.

Far away from us standing with silence,
Silent and calm ready for violence.

I wish to go there in a few years,
And If I don't I will be in tears.

Zainab Musaji (11)
Beaumont Leys School

EARTH!

This is my poem not yours.
It's not about cars or doors.
It's my own poem,
my very own poem.

You can read with your eyes and hands,
but it's not about magical lands.
It's a very good poem, you'll agree.
It's all about you and me.

You can see it everywhere you turn.
If you look close enough you'll learn.
It's not blue cotton and turf.
It's the blue sky and earth.

Luke Taylor (12)
Beaumont Leys School

MILLENNIUM

It's just another day,
of another week,
of another month,
of another year.
So what's so special about this year?
Is it to be looked forward to,
or is it to be feared?
All the promotion,
the Millennium Dome.
I think I might just stay at home
or maybe I will go out,
to see what the millennium is all about.

Chloe Axon (13)
Beaumont Leys School

THE PROWLER

I saw her last
As she crept along the wall.
She tapped on my window sill as the rain began to pour.
She felt along the wall to see if there was a way in.
I heard her howl as she fell up the steps.
She'd just banged her shin.
The handle on the back door then began to turn.
I closed my eyes and tried not to listen.
My ears began to burn,
The prowler came in,
I hid under my bed.
Then in burst Gran,
'Happy Birthday,' she said.

Renée Henny (14)
Beaumont Leys School

DREAMS

A dream is a puzzle waiting to be solved,
A dream is a jigsaw waiting to be unscrambled.

A dream is a vague picture,
But it seems so real.

A dream helps you make sense of things,
In a troubled world.

We dream at night,
We dream in the day.

A dream is someone's secret
Which no one should ever find the key to.

Sonal Bhuptani (13)
Beaumont Leys School

FOR YOU, FROM ME

For the person who always had a laugh,
For the person who knows my secrets,
For the person, that very special person,
Who will always be my friend.

For the animal who listened to my problems,
For the animal who put up with my temper,
For the animal, that very special animal,
That will always be my dog.

For the person who wiped away those tears,
For the person who was always there for me,
For the person, that very special person,
Who will always be my mum.

Layla Goacher (13)
Beaumont Leys School

NEARLY 14

I don't know how
I don't know why
I really want to touch the sky.

Seeing new people in the street
There are still more people I can meet
They do not know what's in my past
They do not know I was always last
At singing, dancing, acting too
If you are bad - I'm worse than you
I dream of a place where I will be
A whole lot more than what they see.

Amanda Steele (13)
Beaumont Leys School

FLYING

I had a dream that I was flying
High up in the deep blue sky.
I then woke up, sighing
I knew I couldn't fly that high.

I sat up thinking in my bed
I would try and fly, just like I'd dreamed
I jumped off my bed and landed on my head
It wasn't as easy as it seemed.

I imagined I was a bird
A flying little blue tit.
Wait a minute, this is absurd
Or is it?

Priscilla Parmar (13)
Beaumont Leys School

LOVE IS . . .

Love is Valentine's Day,
Love is romance,
Love is a bunch of blood-red roses.

Love is romantic music,
Love is hugging,
Love is sitting under the stairs.

Love is nice things,
Love is flowers,
Love is watching the sun set.

Are you in love?

Jodi Brindley (12)
Beaumont Leys School

COLOURS

White like paper
As blank as my mind.

Black like ink cartridges
I can never find.

Orange is an orange
Juicy as can be.

Red is a rose
It smells lovely to me.

Blue is my pen
I use it for writing.

Green is an apple
I really like biting.

Jake Lambert (11)
Beaumont Leys School

BUTTERFLIES

Butterflies flutter in the sky,
As the moon passes by.

They land on a flower,
And down comes a shower
And washes the little butterflies away.

The butterflies didn't come back,
They had gone for a little play.

They had gone to a place
Where they couldn't get washed away ever again.

Amy Senescall (13)
Beaumont Leys School

S-T-R-E-T-C-H-I-N-G

Waking up in the morning is beautiful,
Especially when you have a s-t-r-e-t-c-h,
The tension on your arms is severe,
But you can let it go,
Just by having a s-t-r-e-t-c-h.

When you lift up your arms,
The stress of your legs will disappear,
It seems like you are taller,
But after a while it runs out
And it's over.

Dipen Shah (13)
Beaumont Leys School

PEACE

Peace, she has a face made up of tender, soft lips,
Her eyes are like sparkling diamonds.
Her heart is pumped by caring thoughts,
And her mind is a garden of gentle soft kisses . . .
She glides around the world like a swift bird,
Her hair is a hundred soft roses . . .
Robes and gowns made of peaceful dreams,
And her feet rest on happy thought sandals.
At even the sound of war she cries out loud and pushes it away!
For all the time her mind is on love and kindness . . .
Long gloves of silky daydreams,
Never, ever would she hurt a living thing,
All day, every day, she concentrates on the world . . .
Keeping it *peaceful!*

Chloé French (11)
Leicester Grammar School

THE KIDS AREN'T ALRIGHT

Seeing the world a kid's way,
A nightmare for adults you think.
But deep down inside, there's a kid that you hide,
It's all part of the adult's strange link.
The links are all made up of sections,
Work, rest and TV
But left all alone, with a very dull tone,
Is the kid part neglected you see.
It contains all the past memories,
Of childhood, fun and all play.
N64's and playing with balls.
'The kids aren't alright,' adults say.
Adults they don't understand,
The kid section they're still trying to fight.
But every day, they still always say that
'Hey! The kids aren't alright.'

Simon Kemp (11)
Leicester Grammar School

GHOSTLY IMAGES

Her heart was pounding furiously,
As she stumbled through the icy rain.
The puddles reflected images,
Of evil, death and pain.

Her jet black hair waved madly in the howling wind,
The night in front of her snarled and hissed.
It was a hand trying to grab her,
Pulling her into the depths of the gloomy mist.

Vibha Sharma (12)
Leicester Grammar School

THE JOURNEY

She trickles down the mountainside,
A young child in the sun.
She shimmers and glistens on her way,
And singing her babbling song.
Fast, she flows past mountain goats,
Carrying fish, all quick and silver.

Through some fields she now meanders,
Now gliding into town,
A tributary friend she meets,
As she widens her slender figure,
By eating up her banks.

On through the countryside she cuts her path,
But a fall is soon to come,
Raging, she dives to meet the rocks
Bubbling and churning, furiously she goes.

On and on through industry she flows,
But she stops off for a break,
As curving she leaves her waste behind.

And now she reaches her destination,
Still glittering, clear and smooth,
She meets her husband to whom she gives herself.
The river and the sea.

Caitlin Scott (11)
Leicester Grammar School

SMILE

How do you win when you've already lost?
Smile!
How can you be sure that you'll end up a hero?
Smile!
How can you be friendly without speaking?
Smile!
It will brighten up someone's day.

Poonam Kanabar (11)
Leicester Grammar School

FRIENDS

There is a man called Dave
Who always gives me a wave.
He lives across the road,
Has a giant pond with a giant toad.
He lives at number 8
And has a rusty gate.

I have a friend called John
Whose toes are very long.
When he walks down the street,
People laugh and say, 'Have a look at his feet.'
His toes are as hard as rocks
That rip holes in his smelly socks.

I know a bloke called Chris
Who always blows me a kiss.
I don't know what to do
And he has a wife called Sue
OK, I realise the man is gay.

Keelan Phillips (14)
St Paul's RC School, Leicester

THE DISCO

When I think of a disco I hear
Money jingling ready to be spent on crisps or drinks,
Children laughing
And children shouting.
The DJ shouting through the microphone,
CDs and tapes clicking into their machines,
The humming of music,
The sound of feet stamping as people are dancing
And the sound of people singing in a talent contest or along to songs.
Glasses clinking,
And people munching their food, their plates clashing together.
People chatting to each other
And the pop and rock and roll music.
Doors slamming as people are coming in,
And the toilet door squeaking.
People screaming as smoke comes out the smoke machine,
And at the end I hear the patter of feet going out the door,
And my ears singing as the music is turned off.

Corinne White (12)
St Paul's RC School, Leicester

SMELLS

I love the smell of petrol in the petrol station.
I love the smell of flowers on a fresh autumn day.
The smell of food is nice when you're hungry.
Disinfectant smells weird, but I like it.
A bonfire smells good on a cold, arctic night.
I hate the smell of coffee, onions and lemons.
Pepper makes me cough and splutter.
I hate medicine because it reminds me of hospitals.

Jodie Sutherland (12)
St Paul's RC School, Leicester

GHASTLY DREAMS!

I am
a scary ghost
that only comes at night.
I'll be in dreams beside you
and you'll wake up with a fright!

How will you kill me?
You'll never ever know,
and if you do find out
show me where to go!

The next time I see a body
I'll definitely feed,
and if you want to get away
you'll have to beg and plead.

I am
in a ghost pack
that you'll never want to know,
and if you do see them
you'd really want to go!

I am
really bad,
so bad it seems
that when I see prey
my big eyes gleam!

It's the end of the day,
night is near,
hooray, hooray
I smell fear!

Hallowe'en is near
I can't wait,
there's only one thing I'm looking forward to,
being *scare of the year!*

Ashley Alfonso (12)
St Paul's RC School, Leicester

I Am Noisy

I am:

The loud chattering engine of a Vauxhall Cavalier.
The deafening pneumatic drill.
A riotous football crowd cheer.

I am:

A blaring history teacher.
The ear-piercing rock concert speaker.
A crying baby heard on the radio receiver.

I am:

A low-flying jumbo jet.
Next door's barking pet.
The bang of thunder up above.

I am:

The slam as the homework pile hits your desk.
The turbulent voice of your sisters singing.
An uproar of your grandma's old musical films.

I am:

A strident Spice Girl song.
The bash on your brother's big drum.
The shouting as your mother calls you for dinner.

Adil Jaffer (12)
St Paul's RC School, Leicester

THE GHOST

I see a ghost walking round.
I see the ghost, it's white.
I see the ghost looking at me.
I see the ghost opening doors.
I see the ghost's pimply face.
I see the ghost dancing round.
I feel the ghost creeping up on me.
I feel the ghost walking round me.
I feel the ghost touching me.
I feel the ghost running after me.
I hear the ghost running after me.
I hear the ghost walking round.
I hear the ghost talking to himself.
I hear the ghost banging doors.
I hear the ghost singing to himself.

James Mullarkey (11)
St Paul's RC School, Leicester

MY SMELLY POEM

I hate the smell of my dad's socks, they leave me feeling dizzy,
He does a lot of walking, because he's very busy.
Mustard really stinks when it lingers in my fridge,
And as for onions they make me cry and feel sick.

When I go into a fishmonger it mings and mongs of fish
And together with babies nappies, I dread the thought of them.
I hate the smell of my uncle's dog, his breath is such a stench.
When he comes near me I fall off my bench.
When I smell the country air it turns my stomach into despair.
I wish these smells would not linger and leave my nose alone.

Sean Madden (11)
St Paul's RC School, Leicester

A Smile Which Could Light Up A Room!
(Dedicated to our friend Catherine O'Neill who died earlier this month of cancer, let her rest in peace).

Although she was ill,
She never gave up hope,
Even though she knew,
Her life was getting nearer the end.

She treated everyone the same,
With a friendly smile,
That lit up the room that she entered.

Everyone who knew her,
Would say the same thing,
That she was a loving person,
Who cared about everyone before herself.

But now she has gone,
We feel a great loss,
But still we have our memories.

Helen McEvoy (13)
St Paul's RC School, Leicester

Poison Fear

As I creep through the jungle
I see a shadow of death.
I dare not go near it,
It holds a poison which can kill in six seconds.
It leaps in the air like a catapult.
It waits for the right moment to strike.
It looks harmless but believe me it's not.
The reptile has a navy blue back and the rest of it is red.

Kevin Spencer (13)
St Paul's RC School, Leicester

BOWLING TRIP

I always look forward to bowling,
Even though I'm useless at it,
But today was going to be different,
We were going to enjoy every bit.

We arrived at the centre quite nervous,
We got all dressed up in our kit,
When I just happened to glance in the next lane,
And saw some lads who were really quite fit.

We tried our best to bowl,
But really we were trying to flirt.
Our bowling wouldn't impress them,
Not even my very short skirt.

They came over after a while
To see if we wanted a drink,
A Jack Ryder lookalike decided to sit next to me,
I really tried to look cool and I did, I think.

I was enjoying our really long chat,
But one of his friends came over
With a bowling ball in his hand,
I really need a lucky clover.

As his mate came closer
I took a gulp of my drink,
Then suddenly his mate dropped something on my foot,
A bowling ball which was bright pink.

As I screamed in pain,
I sprayed my Coke
All over his white shirt,
This was beyond a joke.

He wasn't impressed
Cos now he was scruffily dressed,
So he went and we never returned.

Sophie Bowman (12)
St Paul's RC School, Leicester

MEAN MONSTER

It comes at night
stalking its prey.
Knocking them down
and they fall
dead.
But
one man survives.
He sees the monster
and challenges the monster
to a fight.
In the cloaked streets
he bares his fists
and attacks wildly.
Landing each hit
in the monster's face.
The monster,
bewildered,
gives up.
Never to trouble
the city
again.

John Crookes (11)
St Paul's RC School, Leicester

WHAT IS IT?

I heard a creak,
And I smelt quite a reek
Was it a freak?
I didn't know,
Who or what it was,
Was it alive or dead?
I didn't dare go to bed,
Was it here to get me?
I didn't know,
Will it go away?
Or will it stay?
I went to get my dad,
When I told him he thought I was mad,
So I went back to my room,
And picked up a wooden broom,
Someone opened my door,
So I hit them to the floor,
I turned on the light,
It was just my brother, he gave me quite a fright.
Then it had all gone,
So I decided the job was done.

Marc Noble (13)
St Paul's RC School, Leicester

A POEM ABOUT BABIES

Little pink people,
In warm blankets snug;
You just have to grab them
And give them a hug.

They learn quite a lot,
They're really quite smart;
So, look out you walls,
You're their canvas for art.

They go through a stage,
They need teething rings;
But be wary of fingers
That pinch all your things.

When they learn how to crawl,
Now think very carefully, be wise;
Don't let them get out of your sight
Of course, you'll need two pairs of eyes.

Emily Grant (14)
St Paul's RC School, Leicester

I REMEMBER

New uniform on and clean shiny hair,
I entered the classroom, sat down in a chair.
With plimsolls on and a pencil in my hand,
My kind teacher smiled at me, I knew she'd understand.
I wanted to start school, was a little nervous at first,
But now I'd actually started I've got over the worst.
With kind words and help and lots of fun,
I loved my school life now it had begun.
I'll never forget their kindness and care,
And everything I learned while I was there.
I owe the teachers so much for all of their time,
For the education they taught, forever to be mine.
First entering the hall, there was lots to see,
A wide open space used mainly for PE.
A beautiful cross high on the wall,
For everyone to see one and all.
At mass and assembly we would all pray,
Thanking God for everything in our day.
Just one last word on what I remember,
Is enjoying school life from January to December.

Natasha Chaplin (11)
St Paul's RC School, Leicester

OCTOBER!

October is great, October is cool,
Get out tonight and look like a fool.
Tonight all the stars are out,
All the children are about.

> Out came the witches and the bats,
> On witches' broomsticks are the black cats.
> Pumpkins light up and glow,
> Trick or treating off we go.

It's near the end of Hallowe'en
And everything has been.
I'm flying off on my broomstick
Then I see a piece of music.

Olivia Hollman (12)
St Paul's RC School, Leicester

WHO?

Who sleeps on the streets at night?
Who feels cold and miserable?
Who has no one to care for him?
Who has no good in his stomach?

Who has no one to love him?
Who has an old coat and baggy trousers?
Who has holes in his boots?
Who has nowhere to rest his head?

Who could give him food and warmth?
Who could spare some money today?

You!

Guy Hollidge (12)
St Paul's RC School, Leicester

SALAD CREAM

For eighty-five years it was the only dressing,
It was seen on every table.
Drizzled over lettuce,
And even dribbled over chips.
But it has disappeared off millions of tables,
So what has caused this change?

Well people don't seem to like it anymore,
mayonnaise has taken over the shelves.
Salad cream is slowly getting pushed to a side,
Salad cream has no future.

Once it was the only dressing in the shops,
People had no choice.
But when mayonnaise came on the scene,
It was just another dressing,
Filling another shelf.

So long, salad cream,
This is probably goodbye forever.
You were the benchmark of dressings,
But time has to move on.

Remi Durant (12)
St Paul's RC School, Leicester

WINTER

Wet rainy cold nights
It is snowing clear and white.
Nearly here, very excited
Tummy's rumbling for Christmas pie
Eating turkey, smells delicious
Ringing bells that I can hear.

Paula Hillier (12)
St Paul's RC School, Leicester

I HEAR

I hear

People shouting and screaming,
People chatting to each other.

I hear

People crunching on bits of food,
People pouring drinks into glasses,
The sipping of drinks,
The ruffling of crisp packets.

I hear

Music playing,
Darts zooming to the dartboard,
People singing to the karaoke
Chairs scraping.

I hear

The bell ringing for the last orders,
The last time the door shuts for the evening,
The last footsteps in the bar,
The light switch being pushed to turn it off.

That's what I hear.

Rachel Heathcote (11)
St Paul's RC School, Leicester

FEAR!

This fear comes out at night,
When I cannot find the light,
I look around and start to panic,
My thinking starts to go all manic.

I tried with all my might,
To really try and win this fight,
But I still get a fright at
The dead of night.

Lauren Callan (13)
St Paul's RC School, Leicester

TOM KITTEN

Once upon a time there were three little kittens,
Their names were Tom, Moppet and Mittens,
One day Mrs Tabitha Twitchit
Saw they were dirty and decided to fix it.

First she scrubbed, and then she rubbed
Until their coats were a different colour.
Then she sighed and said, 'What a job for a mother.'

She dressed them up smartly,
But Tom had grown partly
So his clothes didn't fit any more.
The buttons flew off,
And his mum sewed them back on but oh it was such a bore.

When they were ready she put them all out,
And told them not to walk much about.
But they didn't do as they were told
Because they ran about, bounced around and rolled.

Their mother was cross,
And so were they at the loss
Of their playtime and of their dinner,
So at the end of the day
They had no play and they were all a bit thinner.

Clare Nelson (12)
St Paul's RC School, Leicester

Again And Again And Again

I can see
colours,
blue, red, green.

I can see
yellow,
as yellow as the sun.

I can see
green,
as green as the grass can be.

I can see
red,
as red as autumn leaves.

Some day I hope you can see
the same things as me
again and again and again.

Rachel Dawes (11)
St Paul's RC School, Leicester

Why?

Some people don't get food
Or don't get loved by their mum and dad,
Or get to have good clothes like us.
We are very lucky,
Some children don't get a chance to go to school,
As we do.
Children don't even get a chance to taste chocolate,
Or get to try a little sweet.

We should do something about it!

David Owen (12)
St Paul's RC School, Leicester

SEASONS

Seasons are cold,
Seasons are warm.
We play when it's sunny,
We stay in for the storms.

In early months
We wrap up tight.
As darkness falls,
Snow is in sight.

It gracefully falls
Without a sound
Like a soft, white blanket,
It covers the ground.

March, April, May,
Are full of new life.
Birds sing their sweet song,
No troubles or strife.

As time moves on,
The next season draws near.
Loud rays of light,
Begin to appear.

People book their holidays,
Families pack their bags.
'Are we nearly there yet?'
The little children nag.

Before you know it,
Autumn's here.
Leaves have fallen,
Christmas is near!

Roberta Mendes (13)
St Paul's RC School, Leicester

Noisy I Ams

I am,
A speeding bullet shot from a gun,
Bang! Bang! Bang!
A hammer striking metal,
Clang! Clang! Clang!
An ear hearing big dogs barking,
Woof! Woof! Woof!
A charging steam train,
Chuff! Chuff! Chuff!

I am,
A builder drilling,
Whiz! Whiz! Whiz!
A popping champagne bottle,
Fizz! Fizz! Fizz!
A motorbike revving up its engine,
Vroom! Vroom! Vroom!
A drummer banging on his drums,
Thump! Thump! Thump!

I am,
A pumping radio,
Boom! Boom! Boom!
The music blares out,
Boom! Boom! Boom!

A really loud digger,
Crash! Crash! Crash!
A plate smashing,
Smash! Smash! Smash!

Oliver O'Shea (12)
St Paul's RC School, Leicester

THE COG

I wonder what would happen
If a cat loved a dog,
And somehow produced a new pet,
Which was called a cog?
It'd have the sharp teeth of a K9,
And that large black, wet, testing nose,
Then the sensitive hearing of a feline,
With a fast bouncy trot as it goes.
When seeking some grub
It would spot a young cub,
(Or a human child to us).
Then would start to prepare,
By grooming its hair,
And end finally while making a fuss.
The child would say, 'Arrrrh,'
Put their plate on the floor,
And the cog would pinpoint
The food and the door.
Then like a lion prowling and waiting,
It would pick the right moment
To dash to the plate,
And what was for the taking.
As it would gulp
Its slender body and long, sharp snout
Would lightly judder,
And sort of stick out.
While it would be finishing off the feast,
In its secret hiding place,
The owner would start to regret the idea
Of making this new and hope to be improved race.

Olivia Brown (13)
St Paul's RC School, Leicester

THE TAMWORTH TWO

It all happened a year or two ago,
In an abattoir not far from here,
The squealing pigs seemed to know their fate,
And that's when they started to fear.

They were getting worried and anxious,
They had been in there nearly all day,
Their lives were now nearly over,
So most of them started to pray.

Two were practically wetting themselves,
They were seriously starting to pee,
Then all of a sudden I heard a loud *oink!*
As together they decided to flee.

They broke the barrier keeping them in,
They were heading for the exit,
I've never seen pigs run so fast in my life,
In fact I could hardly believe it.

They ran to the river and plunged straight in,
Leaving their captors with mouths open wide,
They swam and they swam as fast as they could
To the wood on the other side.

For the next few days they wandered free,
And became known as the 'Tamworth Two',
Then a national newspaper rounded them up,
Now they'll no longer be bacon for you!

Sadie Geoghegan (12)
St Paul's RC School, Leicester

HAIRY FACES

Nowadays men have an obsession with beards,
Long beards, short beards, bushy beards, goatee beards.
What is the point of having hair all over your face?
I mean it just ruins your face.

If you grow a beard how hard is it to wash it,
Brush it, cut it, shave it?
What is the point of having hair all over your face?
I mean it just ruins your face.

People with beards must spend a lot of money on shampoo
Or do they only wash once a week to save their skin?
What is the point of having hair all over your face?
I mean it just ruins your face.

Imagine people with a beard on a hot day, they would sweat like a pig,
I for one don't like sweating.
What is the point of having hair all over your face?
I mean it just ruins your face.

How do hairy people shave?
They must need big, big, big razors to shave their beards.
What is the point of having hair all over your face?
I mean it just ruins your face.

Some beards have shape and style
But some beards I don't want to think about.
What is the point of having hair all over your face?
I mean it just ruins your face.

Michael Hall (12)
St Paul's RC School, Leicester

I AM A CHILD OF GOD

I am a child of God,
And He has sent me here.
Has given me an Earthly home,
With parents, kind and dear.
Lead me, guide me, walk beside me,
Help me with all that I must know,
To live with Him some day.

I am a child of God,
And so my needs are great.
Help me to understand His words
Before it grows too late.
Lead me, guide me, walk beside me,
Help me find the way.
Teach me all that I must know,
To live with Him some day.

I am a child of God,
His blessings are in store.
If I but learn to do His will,
I'll live with Him once more.
Lead me, guide me, walk beside me,
Help me find the way.
Teach me all that I must know,
To live with Him some day.

Kiran Lali (12)
St Paul's RC School, Leicester

APRIL

April flowers start to grow
The dandelions start to blow
The sun is shining
The birds are flying

April Fools day has come
It's time for a holiday in the sun
Spring season has come
It's time for fun
This is April
A great month to remember.

Nicholas Rodrigues (12)
St Paul's RC School, Leicester

THE DENTISTS

I sit in the waiting room,
In the deadly silence,
I said to my sister,
'I can't even hear a whisper.
I can feel someone spying on me
Watching everything I do,
Where are you?'
The dentist walks in
And I walked out.
'Get back here
You have nothing to fear.'

I sit in the surgery chair
So long to go down
How unfair.
They shine on you, that huge light
Can't they see or
Do they think it's the middle of the night?

The drill enters your mouth
Searching for your rotting teeth,
The real tooth lies beneath.

Craig Brennan (13)
St Paul's RC School, Leicester

THE GREATEST

Ding, ding, ding, ding, ding!
The fist hits face,
The lights went out!
His opponent had just been floored.
Muhammad Ali had experienced his first victory,
The first of many,
Which would make him the greatest,
~   'The greatest boxer ever!'

Ali was getting ready,
Not Muhammad, but Laila!
It was her first ever fight,
Her father, looking very tense, was ringside.
One punch, thirty-one seconds into the fight was all it took,
Muhammad just stared.
Her first victory,
The first of just how many?

Stephen Kemp (12)
St Paul's RC School, Leicester

LEICESTER TIGERS

A roaring crowd waiting for the game to begin,
Then there's a whistle which makes a small din,
Pass by pass it's well on the way,
Leicester Tigers are a perfect display.

It starts to rain,
But Leicester score again,
A wondrous try,
So good I could cry.

Now the ball is in opposing hands,
Tackles being made with thunderous bangs,
But a try for them, *boo, hiss,*
It's the conversion I hope they miss.

Peep, full-time,
Leicester wins 15-5.
I am so happy,
I have had a brilliant time.

Brett Costello (14)
St Paul's RC School, Leicester

DOCTOR, DOCTOR!

I walk into the doctors and take a look around,
Everyone looks at me and starts to tap the ground.
I step further in and take a seat,
People are still banging their feet.
I wait, I wait and then wait some more,
Finally the doctor opens the door.
'Frost,' he shouts and I stand up,
He looks at me and gets rid of his cup.
I walk to his room and then step in,
The doctor starts to scratch his chin.
'What seems to be the problem sir,
Are you growing unwanted fur?'
I looked at him in a very strange way,
'I had a sore throat yesterday!'
'I'll have to give you some medicine' he said,
'Now go home and get tucked up in bed.'
When I got home I saw my mum,
'He told me to get into bed,
I personally think he's losing his head.'

Andrew Frost (14)
St Paul's RC School, Leicester

THE BEAST ON THE MOORS

Silently, so quietly, the evil beast crawled towards its prey,
Its fur still stained with blood from its victims of yesterday.
The facial expression it wore was totally terrifying,
The carcasses of unfortunate animals remained there lying.
The creature's sharp, khaki-coloured eyes granting a menacing stare,
A cold, chilling breeze filling the evening air.
The beast took another step on the crisp, white snow,
The fate of the prey, the beast did indeed know.
The beast was breathing heavily, panting on the young foal's neck,
The foal, so content, was quietly sipping at the swift, fast-flowing beck.
It shuddered, realising the presence of the predator about to pounce,
So it cantered away, faster and faster, using all of its energy, every
                                                           ounce.
But the beast was right behind him, chasing the poor horse,
Then it dived, the horse was stunned as he was bowled over with force.
The foal struggled and fought, bravery it did not lack,
But the beast tore his flesh, clinging to the foal's back.
The foal then took his last desperate breath,
As the evil creature went for his neck.
He collapsed to the ground, the intense pain he could not bear,
And to let the beast slaughter him hadn't been fair.
But the beast left the site without any trace,
Apart from the dead innocent animal and the blood on the beast's face.

Nicola Lander (12)
St Paul's RC School, Leicester

TARZAN

Tarzan swinging in the trees
Crying 'Aaahh' beneath the leaves.
Tarzan who can never fall
Landed *splat* into a hole.

Trying to scramble out the hole
Every grip he slips and falls.
Will he make it out again?
Make it to his earthen den?

Katharine Montgomery (14)
St Paul's RC School, Leicester

A FRIEND FOR LIFE

In March of the year of '87,
A baby girl was born.
Her head was full of hair like gold,
Her mum gave birth at dawn.

Her parents' names were John and Ange,
And they loved her lots and lots.
In fact, they loved her so, so much,
They bought another cot.

Miranda wondered why this was,
She only needed one!
Then in May of '87
Angela had a son.

At first Miranda hated the son,
He would scream like a banshee all night.
He got all the attention now,
And all he would do is bite.

But soon Miranda came to realise
That this was the end of their strife.
Sam would stick by her if no one would,
Sam was a friend for life.

Miranda Hill (13)
St Paul's RC School, Leicester

AUTUMN TIME

Leaves are brown,
Ice King is claiming
His crown.
People crowding,
Waters freezing,
People catching colds,
People sneezing.
Magical colours,
Dark is rising,
Days are shorter.
Tailors sizing
For winter clothes.
People having fun,
Wishing for summer,
It's breathtaking.

Christopher Freer (11)
St Paul's RC School, Leicester

AUTUMN TIME

It's that time of the year,
The leaves are golden brown.
Leaves are falling all around you,
Conkers brown fall to the ground too.
Walking makes a soft, soft crunching noise,
Windy gusts blow dust around.
Is it colder or is it me?
Days have got shorter,
Some days are bright and sunny,
Others are freezing cold,
But remember it is only one season.

Krishan Patel (11)
St Paul's RC School, Leicester

THE ENTERTAINERS

The curtains open,
The show proceeds.
An audience staring,
Your nerves begin.

It's going well,
The second scene starts like a dream.
You've got the flow,
Your nerves start to go.

The performance is coming to an end,
They say the last lines.
The crowd applaud,
We take a bow and look in awe.

Shreya Budhdeo (13)
St Paul's RC School, Leicester

THE SCRUM

'Steady now boys, and *down!*'
Eight men became one, a tightly packed body,
Moulded into a mighty shoving machine.
A solid, steaming mass of power and strength
Heaves against the opposition.
Props, holding the scrum up
Locks, pulling it together.
Flankers, pushing in from the side,
And the number eight controlling it all from the back.
The struggle continues,
Push for push
Until . . . 'Alright boys, now . . .
Break!'

Rhiannon Evans (13)
St Paul's RC School, Leicester

THE PARK

The birds are swooping swiftly,
In the clear blue sky.
Up into the fluffy clouds,
They're going extremely high.
Sitting with some friends,
Watching the birds fly by.
Sitting quietly in the park looking at the child who cries.
Walking along the gravel path,
Talking about our day,
Smile at the man with the old grey dog,
As he walks away.
The smell of the short green grass,
It's just been freshly cut.
The loud chatter of the squirrels,
As they collect their nuts.
The slowly moving river,
With little children splashing around.
The shouts of happy children playing,
It is a pleasant sound.

Amy McHale (15)
St Paul's RC School, Leicester

FEAR IS . . .

Fear is a shadow lurking on the walls,
Fear is a pit with everlasting calls.

Fear is darkness as you're trying to sleep,
Fear is a noise that is oh so deep.

Fear is something that cannot be said,
Fear is nothing, it's all in your head.

Amy Rogers (13)
St Paul's RC School, Leicester

AFRICA

The dirty water,
The hungry daughter,
You'd even think it is manslaughter.

The endless heat,
The lack of meat,
You'd even think it's a whole life's cheat.

The disease and famine,
We know we can ease their pain,
But they're losing life's game.

We get to go to school,
But we think it's uncool,
When they go, they have to take their own stool.

But wait, help is at hand,
Give it up for Ghana,
Their life is in demand.

Lucy Eccles (12)
St Paul's RC School, Leicester

SUN

I wish I could
go to the sun.
Now wouldn't
that be fun
to fly high
in the sky
all the
way up to the
sun?

Thomas Patrick Owen (11)
St Paul's RC School, Leicester

I WONDER . . .

I wonder why if God made us equal,
we are all different.
I wonder what I could do to
make us all the same.
I wonder who could help me
make a difference to the world.
I wonder where we could go to
make the sick, healthy again.
I wonder.

I wonder why people's relatives
die in tragic circumstances.
I wonder what goes through their
minds.
I wonder who would want to
see their pain.
I wonder where they could go to
leave their past behind.
I wonder.

I wonder why we make people
our slaves to work.
I wonder what they've done to
deserve it, to have no tomorrow.
I wonder who'd care if they died.
I wonder where they can cry at
night and get rid of their sorrow.
I wonder.

Krusha Patel (12)
St Paul's RC School, Leicester

SCHOOL DAYS

Hundreds every day
Pile through those gates,
I know what's coming my way,
It's going to be a long day.

First I've got maths,
What's it all about?
Equations and graphs,
Can't wait to get out.

Next history,
Going back in time,
It's worse than PE,
But I suppose I shouldn't whine.

Now it's science,
Test tube confusion,
The teacher wants silence,
But what's that explosion?

There goes the bell,
We're all free,
That day was hell,
Now home for tea.

Hundreds at night,
Pile out those gates,
All drift out of sight,
And the school stands silent.

Jenny Smith (13)
St Paul's RC School, Leicester

Why?

Why the pain?
Why the sorrow?
Why the hunger?
Why me?

Why the thirst?
Why so different?
Why so unfair?
Why me?

Why the labour?
Why the crowds?
Why me?
Why not them?

Polly Snow, Tanya Coe & Gabriella Kowzan (13)
St Paul's RC School, Leicester

Fear

Dark, glum and eerie the darkness underground,
Weird, unpredictable things waiting to be found,
Silent, dark, bare walls not making a sound,
Old toys, rings and unwanted things all in a mound.

Musty, dusty smell, (not been cleaned for ages),
Unwanted books with ripped out pages,
Dead rats forgotten in their cages,
Cobwebbed diaries of all forgotten family rages.

Creaky floorboards under my feet,
Object in the corner, ugh! Rotten meat!
Something I, definitely don't want to eat,
Spiderweb covered in flies for the spider, what a treat.

Sean Henry (12)
St Paul's RC School, Leicester

MY FAVOURITE COLOURS

Blue is for a flowing river,
A night sky,
Or a wonderful dolphin.

Yellow is a pretty star,
A fierce lion roaring,
Or a bright ray of sunshine.

Green is the thorny grass,
A turtle having a race,
Or an alligator snapping his teeth.

Red is roses being picked,
A bunch of autumn leaves,
Or some sweet strawberries.

Purple is peacock feathers,
A colour of the rainbow,
Or some seedless grapes.

Nabila Jaffer (11)
St Paul's RC School, Leicester

WHO IS THIS MAN?

He's the one with glasses, false teeth and grey.
He's funny and tells jokes, only on a good day.
He's crafty and jolly and happy and fun,
His vest's always dirty, but he's never glum.
Football, golf, cricket the lot,
Knowledge of these, he's sure got.
He loves cleaning shoes, polishes them until they shine,
He's my grandad, the one and only, he's loving and kind.

Sarah Chilton (13)
St Paul's RC School, Leicester

HALLOWE'EN

Hallowe'en is a time for dressing up
In something weird or spooky,
Or wrapped in bandages from bottom to top.
Scary fangs and fake blood too,
Or people sneaking up and yelling *boo!*

As quiet as a mouse, the neighbours wait
For the old-fashioned creak of the gate,
Then the footsteps up to the door,
You twist the knob to hear an almighty *roar!*

'*Trick or treat?*' the terrors say,
In a scary sort of way.
They put out their hand, hope for something back,
Then you reach in your pocket and give them a snack.

Jamie Pelos (13)
St Paul's RC School, Leicester

NOTHING

Children carry water upon their heads,
While at home their family is waiting in sheds.
Hardly any food and polluted water to drink,
Their minds stay alive while their hearts sink.
Disease and illness kills many,
Stirring up nothing, not a penny.
To walk miles every day
While the sun beats down with a powerful ray.
No seeds for a crop,
No buying from a shop.
No singers that sing,
And yet we don't do anything.

Rebecca Keeber (12)
St Paul's RC School, Leicester

THE SUMMER

The summer, when the weather's hot
fields of green everywhere
great weather everyone knows
laughter and smiles in the air.

The sounds of ice-cream vans
pulling up to your road
faces of kids from the first lick.
Holidays! No school! Everyone shouts
daily trips to swimming pools.

Two months, anything goes
no school, *we're free!*
Typically after one
bored sighs, pitiful pleas.

Jan Horbacz (14)
St Paul's RC School, Leicester

THE MILLENNIUM BUG!

It's green, slimy and very, very tall,
It will crash your computer,
But that's not all.

It will slither through the city,
Crushing everything in its path,
Nothing can stop it,
It's just too fast.

Hospitals, banks and lots of other things,
It's all gonna happen
When 12 o'clock rings.

Michael Gilbert (13)
St Paul's RC School, Leicester

AN ANNOYING POEM

I am
The nasty Jack Frost that comes at night,
The mosquito that gives you that painful bite.

The hospital food you are forced to eat
The devil himself you hate to meet.

The humming of a queen bumblebee
The punch harder than Mohammed Ali.

Can be angry, horrible even insane
Like that leader Saddam Hussain.

Colour of a rotten tomato
Stronger than all the people at NATO.

The cramp in your foot right at the bottom
Can talk longer than Dot Cotton.

So clever unlike the monarchy
I'm annoying. Hee! Hee! Hee!

Minaz Shaffi (13)
St Paul's RC School, Leicester

WHY?

Why can't I walk?
Why can't I talk?
Why can't I have fun?
Why don't I have friends?
Why do I have to be like this?
Why can't I be normal?
Why don't people talk to me?
And why can't they see?

Sam Matthews (12)
St Paul's RC School, Leicester

FALL IN WINNIPEG

Orange, yellow, brown and red
Those are the colours I see.

Hazelnut, acorn and chestnut
Those are the nuts I see.

Down the street leaves blow
On the grass are piles of it too.

Everyone's busy, everyone's raking
Quick, quick! Stuff it in bags
Before the snow falls.

It's too bad, it never stays long
For winter is on its way
Oh! How I wish it would stay
For Fall in Winnipeg
Is the best season and that is that.

Elizabeth Bracken (12)
St Paul's RC School, Leicester

WHY?

Why are people less fortunate than us?
Why are people not as wealthy as us?
Why don't people have clothes?
Why don't people have a chance to go to school?
Is this because we are selfish and not giving?
Those people are so happy, friendly and loving,
And would love to have what we have but don't.
So give a little and think of them and think
How well off you are.

Elzbieta Lipinska (12)
St Paul's RC School, Leicester

WHY?

Why don't we all get treated the same?
Why all this sadness, who is to blame?

Why are some people suffering in pain?
Why are so many people on the streets sleeping in the rain?

Why can't we all help each other?
Why can't we care like sister and brother?

Why are some people that are rich doing nothing?
Why can't they get up and do something?

Why are some children in hunger and thirst?
And I'm sure they'll be happy some day,
It can't get any worse.

Helena Obodoagwu (12)
St Paul's RC School, Leicester

YOUR CHANGE WILL CHANGE

One pound a month
is enough to build a water pump
so less fortunate people than us
do not have to walk kilometres.

Sponsor a child
and give them food
a place to sleep
and at least a room.

So a bit of money
or your change
will make a big or the biggest change.

Bernard D'Souza (12)
St Paul's RC School, Leicester

Autumn Is The Best

Autumn is cool except one thing,
Christmas bells aren't causing a ding.
Red, orange, brown and green are the colours of the leaves,
You have to wrap up warm and make sure you've got long sleeves.
I love autumn an awful lot,
But I wish the animals weren't getting ready to sleep in their slot.
The leaves fall off the trees
And I'm starting to feel a little breeze.
Every morning I see a mist,
But I'm still pleased a new season has come which is my wish.
Autumn is my favourite season,
For lots of different reasons.
I could go on all day,
About autumn that is,
But I had better stop now so goodbye.

Jayne Pearson (11)
St Paul's RC School, Leicester

Why Is It Fair?

Why is it fair that we have water running from our taps,
When for their water they have to walk forty laps?
Why is it fair that we get to go to school,
But if they go they have to take their own stool?
Why is it fair that we have loads of clothes,
When they have so many woes?
Why is it fair that we get a roof over our heads,
When they don't know if they'll find a bed?
Why is it fair that we celebrate our birthdays,
But they just sit there and they are thirsty?
But I just have to say 'Why is it fair?'

Pippa Bolton (12)
St Paul's RC School, Leicester

HAND OUTS!

When God (upon a wishing star,)
Did hand out blood and brains,
He gave the love to you and me
And this emotion you can see.
He gave us hope and dreams and sense,
But on others these talents never commence.
We are given from death to birth
As we flourish other new talents do unearth.
We get given the hand outs from God to us,
No handouts for others,
Why? Because . . .
This word is so unfair,
But no talents we can share.
It all started with a little look from father to mother,
From mother to cook who baked the world
And made the bread,
Who never believed in what God said.
Who never thought we all should be equal
From bird to sand from sand to people.
So we all aren't equal, this joins the sequel.
Some are good, some are bad,
Some have less, this makes me mad.
So when all is done, people have less,
People have more,
Others have more reasons to feel insecure.

Clare Harding (12)
St Paul's RC School, Leicester

MY DREAM MACHINE

I have a place inside my head,
Where all my dreams are made,
Everything there is hard to believe,
But nothing ever fades.

All my wildest fantasies can become reality,
I'll always be able to be alone and be who I want to be.
No one can bother me,
Not even the raging sea,
I like being alone just to be me.

Brittany Hays (11)
St Paul's RC School, Leicester

DOMINO

A small black and white cat
The runt of the pack
With little pink paws
And soft, strong jaws.

And as she sleeps
In her favourite spot
Under the radiator
Pleasant and hot.

A small black and white ball
Huddled in the heat,
Purring away
Looking so sweet.

As she awakens
She stretches and yawns
Showing her teeth
They're as sharp as thorns.

A small black and white cat
The runt of the pack
With little pink paws
And soft, strong jaws.

Katherine Mitchelmore (13)
St Paul's RC School, Leicester

BLUE AND GREEN

Blue is the far away sky
Blue is shiny paint
Blue is a fast car
Blue is sparkling eyes
Blue is the shimmering sea
Blue is the beautiful flowers
Blue is the stained glass windows
Blue is our lady's robes.

Green is the grass
Green is the evergreen leaves
Green is the turf at Filbert Street
Green is the colour of conker shells
Green is one of the colours the army use
Green is the colour of my RE book
Green is the colour of apple juice
Green is one of the colours of pencils.

Daniel Clowes (12)
St Paul's RC School, Leicester

AUTUMN LEAVES

Autumn leaves are red, brown and yellow
They fall out of the trees
They get brushed to one side and then down the drain
They disappear the next month
We never know where they go
Autumn leaves curl up when they fall out of the trees
Some of them are golden
Some of them are light brown
Altogether they are the autumn colours.

Abdul-Raheem Arzbegi (12)
St Paul's RC School, Leicester

LESS FORTUNATE

L onely are those poor people
E mpty hearts, no love for them
S ad and weary, a box to live in
S ick because of their addictive habits

F airness they have never known
O nly pain and sorrow
R eady to die, to reach a better place
T his Earth has nothing left to give them
U nity is yet to come
N ever again will they have to suffer
A ll these people, God's *own* people
T raumatised for what they are
E nough of this, they should have their fair share.

James Hadley (12)
St Paul's RC School, Leicester

MY GRANDAD

My grandad is very old
in his ears bristle
the hairs of many
greying years
His neck is folded
with loose cloth
skin that hangs
below a stubble
of a chin
and on his hands
lie the purple veins
lie thick like worms
after the summer rains.

Adam Spriggs (13)
St Paul's RC School, Leicester

AUTUMN COLOURS

Brown leaves on the trees falling to the ground
White webs sparkle with dew
While all the black spiders are watching you
White and brown owls fly through the night air
And all the bears asleep in their dark black lairs
Shiny conkers fall to the ground
While all the black moles asleep in the ground
Shiny white stars in the dark night sky
While I'm eating my veggie pie
Misty grey skies give a warning
While the early Sunday sun is dawning
Red sky at night shepherd's delight
Red sky in the morning shepherd's warning
At the end of an autumn night
Everything gets lit up by the morning sunlight.

Chet Willcock (12)
St Paul's RC School, Leicester

AUTUMN COLOURS

Golden leaves upon the ground
Shiny conkers are all around.
Squirrels collecting acorns and nuts before the winter winds come near.
Frosty mornings, cold and misty,
Many trees are losing leaves.
Enjoy dinners in front of the fire,
Getting dark very early.
Have to wrap up warm on the way to school,
PlayStation at 4.30pm as it would be pitch-black.
Soon it will be Christmas, looking forward to my presents,
Looking forward to the end of autumn.

Alex Stafford (11)
St Paul's RC School, Leicester

LIFE'S DEFEAT

To have to walk eight miles a day just to get some water,
They need some help, they need some care,
What could make their journey shorter?

The children laugh even though they're ill,
We wallow in self pity.
They've never even seen a pill,
We know we're rich,
We think they're poor,
Why is it them that get shown the door?

The pounding sun, they have to bear,
They manage to have fun, though the world doesn't care.
When the armies come they mean to scare,
But in the long term it's our faces we have to wear.
Not the best clothes, not the latest Nikes,
It's time to help, it's time to make things right.

Christie Silk (12)
St Paul's RC School, Leicester

DECEMBER

December is calling
It's getting chilly and wet
It starts to snow
We are all inside
We start to open the presents
And business is going

December is nearly over
January is starting
The winter flowers are flowering
And business starts again.

Chris Evans (12)
St Paul's RC School, Leicester

SPRING MAY

Spring is here, spring is now
Through all times when it's cold
Spring was there to dry my eye
It felt like a real warm tie
Every person in every way
There is hope for a dry time
Rain and cold drafts swooped by
Spring is there to comfort my life
The days that are good, the days are best
May is the month that I love best
Things grow things go clear
But spring goes in a tear
The tear at the start has gone today
But it means spring's here instead
Instead of blood in my heart
Spring is there for a new start.

Karl Reeve (12)
St Paul's RC School, Leicester

THE LONER

The loner sits in the corner,
Watching people coming closer
A solitary man in an overpopulated land;
There's no one around to lend him a hand.
He's isolated inside his mind,
Unfamiliar with all mankind.
Loneliness is a sad thing;
Who knows what troubles it can bring.
I couldn't believe what he said,
'I want to put a bullet through my head.'

Richard Bracken (16)
St Paul's RC School, Leicester

THINKING OF YOU

The day you died so did a part of me,
The day you went away is the day that crushed my heart.
I never got my chance to say goodbye,
To say my farewell.
You were, and still are, a very important part of my life,
I hope you know how much I loved you.
I may not have shown my love for you in the ways that I should
But I loved you.
I know I probably took advantage and never listened but I did care.
Children are like that, they don't know what they have
Until they've lost it.
When I think of you, I always remember the good times, not the bad.
You will always be in my mind and in my heart.
This is the only way I can express the way I feel about you.
I hope somehow you will know this and understand.

Dejana Tomic (13)
St Paul's RC School, Leicester

AUTUMN POEM

Autumn leaves fall
Hear them crunch, hear them crisp
All in bright lovely colours in the park
Lovely and big
Hear the birds tweet, tweet, tweet
Lovely sounds in the park
Children playing, hear them laugh
Look at the parents playing away
Hear the dogs woof, woof
And there's lovely sounds in the park
Lovely sounds in the park.

Jade McNulty (11)
St Paul's RC School, Leicester

HOW A GIRL OF 11 SHOULD BEHAVE

Don't get into a single little fight,
Help with the shopping on Saturday night.
Always go to bed at nine o'clock
And always make sure you wear a pretty frock.
Never, ever, ever swear,
Be polite and do not stare.
Stand up straight and keep your chin up,
Never slurp when drinking from a cup.
Do not give a promise you cannot keep
Or else you'll go upstairs and go to sleep.
Get up at seven and go to school,
Do everything you're told, do not break a rule.
Don't forget to just be you,
Think about others and yourself too.

Rachael Ramkissoon (11)
St Paul's RC School, Leicester

MY FAVOURITE COLOUR

Red is an apple shining on the tree
Red is the rose, oh so pretty
Red is the raspberry very, very sweet
And red is the pepper that's spicy to eat.

Red's my favourite colour because it's so bright
A red sheet is used in a bull fight
My nose goes red on a cold, cold day
Red's the best colour I don't care
What anyone may say.

I love red because it's bright and great to see
Without the colour red I wouldn't be me.

James Dawes (12)
St Paul's RC School, Leicester

To Belong

Smiling and talking,
But it's still there:
Underneath the front I show
I'm standing there,
But I'm not:
I'm miles away and drifting further,
Waiting to be saved,
To belong.

Silent and alone,
And it's still there:
Deep inside every part of me.
I want to be happy,
But I'm not:
I'm miles away and sinking deeper,
Wishing to be saved,
To belong.

Claudine Carletti (16)
St Paul's RC School, Leicester

How A Girl Of 11 Should Behave

Do the shopping for your mum,
Don't watch TV until your homework is done
Tidy your room until it's nice and clean
And never, ever, ever be mean
Get up at six and go to school
Behave yourself and don't act cool
Don't get too tied up in being good
Leave some time for you as everyone should.

Naomi Kalkun (11)
St Paul's RC School, Leicester

SMELLS

Chocolate cooking in a pan
Uncle Brian's musty van
Roses soft and silky sweet
Ice-cream, mmmm, such a treat
Bunsen burners all in school
Peppermint toothpaste - smells cool
Creamy, yummy melted butter.
If you don't like the smell of chips
You're a nutter!
Fresh cut pine
Apple pie, yum all mine
Dinner ready on a plate,
Summer barbecues, there's a smell I do not hate,
Coffee freshly ground
Baking bread smells sound
Onions frying
Warm clothes just finished drying.

Katherine Doniak (11)
St Paul's RC School, Leicester

LESS FORTUNATE

Lots of lonely people
Sleeping on the streets
Everyone of them wondering
If they're going to eat
Selling lots of dope and drugs
Trying to make some money
Sleeping in the park's no joke
So please don't think it's funny.

Joseph Faulkner (12)
St Paul's RC School, Leicester

THE LIONESS

The long fire burnt, grass swayed
in the sandy breeze,
She laid there staring
eyes fixed
as if she was dead.
No one could see her only
the eyes above.
Then
as fast as a bullet
she sprinted across
the open plains
getting closer
and closer
to her prey!

Anna Snee (13)
St Paul's RC School, Leicester

THE FIRE WITHIN

Hate:
An emotion difficult to explain,
Overwhelming me like a tidal wave,
Crashing against my heart,
Filling me from inside out with knots,
Wringing me dry of compassion.

Hate:
Once planted grows into an oak,
Taking control of my thoughts and senses,
Entwining itself into the caverns of my soul,
Leaving only a flicker of mercy to act as an axe.

Frances Andrew (17)
St Paul's RC School, Leicester

YOU

People rush by, busy,
But surrounded by others.
Watching them, dizzy,
I wish we were together.

Lost, gone forever,
However it is said,
We'll never again be together,
Never regain the life we led.

Good times I remember,
Though I carry on,
Deep in my heart, lasting forever,
Are memories of
You.

Selina D'Sa (16)
St Paul's RC School, Leicester

UNTITLED

I'm bound with all the weight of words that I've tried to say,
I'm chained to places all around I've never wished to stay.
The deepest, darkest ocean strives not with my fears,
With dread I am engulfed of drowning in my tears.

Damn my situation and the games I have to play,
Not least this passing hour, but every single day.
An hour is a lifetime, a day is longer yet
Time is no fine healer when contentment is in debt.

I lead not by example and leave my words though small,
Make your friends from Lego, 'cause Lego builds a wall.

Helen Morris (17)
St Paul's RC School, Leicester

SWEETS, CHOCOLATE

Chewy sweets, sticky sweets,
All different kinds to try
Fat and thin, long and short,
There's lots for you to buy.

Past the postbox near the sweet shop,
On the way to school,
Shall it be liquorice sticks, white mice,
Torpedoes or a chocolate tool?

Decisions, decisions, all different sorts of kinds,
In such a hurry, but I simply must make up
My mind.

My time is running very short,
The other boys have been and bought -
Mrs Smith is telling me
Maybe I'll save my pocket money and come tomorrow,
Then I'll see!

Jemma Ford (13)
St Paul's RC School, Leicester

CATS

Cats sleep anywhere
Any table, any chair.
Top of a piano, window ledge
In the middle, on the edge
Open drawers, empty shoes
Anybody's lap will do
Fit in a cardboard box
With your frocks.

Siobhan Ann Hirrell (11)
St Paul's RC School, Leicester

FEAR!

I see the plane come into the runway.
I see two old friends joking and laughing as
they climb into the hatch.
I am the last one and they close the door,
I am now trapped.
I hear the motors start and the plane
begins its slow motion.
I hear the click of the radio as it is turned on.
I hear the person by me say that this is
his favourite song.
I hear the hatch opening again,
The air rushing out and in as a man heaves on it.
My way out.
My stomach gets tighter as I get further
down the line.
I feel the adrenaline running as I try to
get enough courage to jump.
The air rushes past me and I try to pull my cord,
then look at it in my hand.
I feel fear,
I feel the ground.

Alastair Swinfield (13)
St Paul's RC School, Leicester

FEAR

What if the ropes split when I abseil?
What if the dog next door attacks me?
What if I fall down and my heart fails?
What is I drown and am lost at sea?

What if I get ill and they want to operate?
What if it goes wrong and they give me too much anaesthetic?
What if I get mugged and impaled on a gate?
What if my family and friends eat bad food and get sick?

What if I fail my GCSEs and have to resit?
What if I'm sent to jail for things I haven't done?
What if I get a skin condition and die from it?
What if I grow up alone, never having any fun?

What if I get trapped in rubble after a hurricane?
What if I'm abandoned and sold as a slave?
What if I get stuck in a lift and come out insane?
'What if' says gran, 'you worry yourself into an early grave?'

Louisa Atkin (14)
St Paul's RC School, Leicester

MY NOSE ALARM

Hair gel, toothpaste, start the day,
Voodoo, Java which one I say.
McDonald's would give me such a lift
But I make do with salt and vinegar crisps.
Eyes shut tight, I pass the farm
How do I know? My nose alarm.
Sniffs manure, smoke and dog
Easy to detect, even in fog.
Pencil case, plastic, glue, ink
Can only mean school stinks!
Dictionary, hamster, smells all around,
My home by whiffs will be found.
I pass the aviary, bird droppings I know
I'm sure they're putting on a show.
The next place, dog mess where you tread,
Must be the park, Mum always sees red.
But what's this smell, bad or good?
Sweaty shinpads, oils and mud.
Can only mean one thing to me
The greatest game there'll ever be.

Adam Chilton (11)
St Paul's RC School, Leicester

BLOODTHIRSTY

I am a nasty vampire,
and I'd love to suck your blood.
I'm a truly evil creature,
that just cannot be good.

I lie in wait so sneakily,
a graveyard's where I prey.
you can be safe if you are near,
but only in the day.

This is because that's when I sleep,
I'm only out at night,
and if you come across me,
you'll get a nasty bite.

Can you guess in what I sleep?
A satin lined black coffin
and if I get a hold of you,
that's just what you'll be off in.

I can really hurt you,
my fangs will make you scream,
if I should get a grip of you
you'll wish it was a dream.

If you're brave enough to try
and rid the world of me,
there's just one thing that you can do,
if you dare to come and see.

You will need a wooden stake,
it is your deadly dart,
come over to the graveyard
and drive it through my heart.

If you aren't scared and think you're brave,
Then you can put me in my grave.

Nicholas Dunkley (12)
St Paul's RC School, Leicester

HOW I FEEL?

Am I feeling the way that I am
Because of what happened
A second,
A minute,
An hour,
Before?

Or it could be something that I experienced
A day,
A week,
A month,
Before.

A year,
A decade,
Another lifetime,
Before.

I can't decide how I'm feeling,
Or why I am this way,
It really is confusing me,
I hope this feeling will go away.

Joanna Siwek (16)
St Paul's RC School, Leicester

THE EAGLE

There I see him sitting on his rock,
Proud, majestic, king of the birds,
Watching, waiting, eyes glowing,
Hard, cold and calculating,
Ready to swoop at any time.

Suddenly he's off,
Flying high in the sky
This huge bird, graceful,
Riding with the wind,
Not making a sound
He attacks like a bullet from a gun
In a split second,
His poor unsuspecting prey is clutched up
By his huge talons,
Back to his rock he goes - triumphant,
Ready to enjoy his feast.

Rick Tooley (13)
St Paul's RC School, Leicester

OCTOBER DELIGHT

The autumn leaves blowing in the breeze
Knocking off the apples from the old tree
The world is a mix of brown and red
Whilst the leaves on the ground make a golden bed
Squirrels leap about through the day
The frost spreads through the trees in every way
The children go out in Hallowe'en dress
Only for the trick or treating to end up in a mess
October is here, summer has gone
For the autumn is here and it's going to be long.

Camilla Bell (12)
St Paul's RC School, Leicester

LONELY I AMS

I am unpopular
With nothing to look forward to
Sad
'Cause no one's around you
Lonely
Then someone comes up to you
Shy
They run away from you.

I am gentle
With no harm inside me
Nervous
When someone tries to speak to me
A dog
Which no one ever owns up to
A cold
That no one ever catches.

Lisa Rowley (12)
St Paul's RC School, Leicester

CHRISTMAS AT HOME

There was excitement in the cold, frosty air.
It was that time of year, *Christmas.*
The colourful lights and flashy decorations were up.
The carol singers were singing cheerfully
and the robins were darting from gate to gate.
I could hear the banging of crackers
and the snapping of wood in the fire.
The children were playing in the fluffy white snow,
looking for Santa.
Laughing and cheering is the sign of Christmas at home.

Chris Marczak (14)
St Paul's RC School, Leicester

CHOCOLATE

Chocolate, chunky delicious chocolate,
Melting in your mouth until smooth.
Chocolate, all different beautiful flavours,
Plain, milk, white, orangey and minty cool.

Sweets, succulent, attractive, likeable sweets
Rotting your teeth but you can't resist temptation.
Sweets, boiled, sugared, soft or gummy,
To not eat all the sweets in the world you need patience.

Chunky chocolate, succulent sweets,
All of these lovely treats,
But what do you get? Vile vegetables which
Taste like smelly feet!

Luke Andrew (13)
St Paul's RC School, Leicester

CHRISTMAS

It's here! It's here!
Joyful Christmas is here.
Running down the stairs in laughter and excitement.
All the presents, it's overwhelming.
Opening your enormous presents with a genuine, angelic smile.
It's here! It's here!
The gentle, warm smell of Christmas is here.
It's wonderful, no! Better, it's brilliant.
All your caring family is here.
You can feel the pleasant love around you.
The special day comes once a year and is delightful.
It's here! It's here!
Great, Christmas is here.

Michele Powell (14)
St Paul's RC School, Leicester

THE CAT

The cold cramped crooked alley, as dark as night,
Had two small animals in,
One was a mouse, the other a cat.
The cat sat there as still as a statue,
The mouse was picking food from a knocked over bin.
The mouse felt it was being watched,
It span round to see!
Two emerald green eyes reflecting light.
A car went past lighting up the alley revealing
Emptiness . . . (It had begun to move!)
The mouse turned, ran down the cold, cramped, crooked
Alley, ran like the wind!
But it was too late. The cat pounced on him like
Lightning and with one quick slash!
Silence . . .

David Biggins (13)
St Paul's RC School, Leicester

THE CHEETAH

Cheetah fast and fierce,
Looking cautiously for unsuspecting prey,
Waiting,
Watching,
Ready to pounce at any second,
Observing its prey sleek and quiet.

At last prey is sighted in one second, cheetah is in control,
Its prey left in ruins of wounds,
Cheetah still feeding on bloody prey.

Ashleigh Spriggs (13)
St Paul's RC School, Leicester

MY NEAR MISS

It stretched out as far as the eye could see,
Shimmering silver as cool as ice.
It curled around my toes like a small snake,
I lowered myself into this bottomless pit,
Not knowing if a white shark might decide to have an early lunch.
I braced myself, hit something hard,
Was it rocks or another predator?
I had to get away from this thing,
So I threw my hands forwards and pulled them back.
My legs were kicking furiously, I had to get away,
If only I could reach the other side.
When oh oh, suddenly it got me.
It pulled me out of the water and was holding me up above it.
I looked down, it was the enemy coming to eat me up,
It pulled me nearer.
I squeezed my eyes shut and let out a big scream,
Was this to be the end?
Was I to die at five years old?
I tried to say my prayers before it got me,
But I was too late, or was it to be?
He came and gave me an enormous cuddle.

Rebecca Ard (14)
St Paul's RC School, Leicester

ANOTHER YEAR

Summer is so hot, you can't get to sleep,
With sounds of cricket, through grass as they leap,
Summer is late nights and later lie-ins,
Then eat all day, to build up your chins.

Autumn is crimson leaves, thick upon the ground,
Autumn is walking to a crisp, crunching sound,
Autumn is back to school, another fresh year,
This is why autumn's the season I fear.

Winter is cold toes, pink cheeks and nose,
Winter is wrapped up in bundles of clothes,
Winter is dark nights and cold frosty mornings,
Winter is filled with severe weather warnings.

Spring brings warmth and an abundance of flowers,
Daffodils, tulips, I could go on for hours,
The winter is over, the world begins to colour,
All in the build-up to another year's summer . . .

Scott Madden (15)
St Paul's RC School, Leicester

I HEAR

I hear my guardian angel talking to me,
Telling me where to go,
What path to take,
What my life should be,
I hear music from Heaven,
The music of a harp,
I then hear music blaring out next door,
Keeping me up all night.

I hear the clock of my life ticking away,
Tick-tock, tick-tock, tick-tock.
I hear my heart beating soon to stop one day,
I hear guns on TV,
People explaining how they are trying to survive the war,
I still can hear my sister crying,
I can hear my mother shouting,
Faintly I can hear my brother reading quietly as a mouse,
Then all at once everything went quiet,
I couldn't hear a thing.

I hear.

Grace Bomken (12)
St Paul's RC School, Leicester

THE LITTLE BUNNY

'Look at my ears'
The little rabbit cries
'They're much too big
For a bunny my size.'

She hops in the field
Where cane is tall,
'I like mouse's ears
They're round and small.'

'Squirrel's ears are
Much smaller than mine.
Ears like squirrels
Would suit me fine.'

Little bunny wandered
Through the forest all day.
She didn't pay attention
Now she's lost her way.

Suddenly from far away,
She heard her mother's call
'My ears are good for listening
I like them after all!'

Damien Delano Silcott (14)
St Paul's RC School, Leicester

THE BONFIRE

Burning brightly in the night
So tantalising is the sight,
Bonfire, bonfire you are so fierce!
So hot and exciting,
Your flames look like nymphs!
Dancing around.

Bangs and booms!
What a lot of sounds,
Fireworks like gunshots
Towering up into the soundless sky.

Thomas Robson (11)
St Paul's RC School, Leicester

CHRISTMAS

Buy, buy, buy.
Sell, sell, sell.
People rush,
Eyes sparkle.

Tension builds,
Emotions flow in torrents,
Happiness rises and falls in tides,
Tired shoppers alive and smiling.

Bubbly, fizzing, eccentric faces,
Presents, parcels, food and drink.
Decorations glow,
Growling children scream, shout, dance and sing.

Preparations done,
Expectant faces overlook actions,
'Dinner is served,'
Breathless you feed.

It's over for another year,
Silence,
Tranquil,
Peace.

Edward Martin (15)
St Paul's RC School, Leicester

MY DAY TRIP!

The log flume was huge
The water was cold
We started to sing
We were all feeling bold

Then all of us screamed
Our faces were white
The ride was so huge
It was a terrible fright

We didn't eat food
Until after the ride
We had popcorn and candyfloss
And potatoes when fried

The day was too short
It was time to go home
We were all feeling tired
This is the end of my poem.

Samantha Milankovic (14)
St Paul's RC School, Leicester

JULY

July is here
And out comes the sun
As I walk along the sandy pier
Remembering last July where
I had lots of fun
In July there can be some windy days
But it is not that cold
We want the sun to always stay
Until the autumn folds.

Nadia De Marco (12)
St Paul's RC School, Leicester

PEPPER CAT

There she goes
with her pink paws.
On the end are
her scratchy claws.

There she goes
with her whiskers long.
She starts to purr,
it's like a song.

There she goes
with her saucer wide eyes.
Then she leaps
such a surprise.

There she goes
just like that.
My black and white killer
my Pepper cat.

Emma Cartwright (13)
St Paul's RC School, Leicester

SMELL

I like the smell of Mum's perfume,
I like the smell of flower bloom,
I like the smell of fresh grass,
I like the smell of clean brass,
I like the smell of bubblegum,
I like the smell of strong rum,
I like the smell of yellow hay,
I like the smell of grey clay.

Carl Tooke (11)
St Paul's RC School, Leicester

I AM AMAZED

I am
Amazed at where one sock goes
When my mum does the wash
And when she's on the telephone
Her voice goes really posh.

I am
Amazed how my little brother could
Always find my secret things
And while I'm on the toilet
The phone always rings.

I am
Amazed at my mum
Who always seems to know
When my arms and legs are hurting
That all I need to do is grow.

But last of all, I'd like to know
When I'm poorly with a bug
How my mum always knows
That all I want is a little hug.

Lynette Dahou (12)
St Paul's RC School, Leicester

A LOVE AFFAIR WITH HER

I love Her but no one forbids it,
Yet I am as female as She,
This love was made to break all the rules,
For I love Her like She is a he.

She's beautiful in her pallor,
Her face the most radiant white,
Yet She hides it from me in the daytime,
For She's at her most stunning at night.

It's then that She's all in her glamour
Her midnight jewels flatter her beauty;
I can't help but gaze into Her face,
As She gazes back at me.

Now if our love should ever wane,
I shall not change my tune,
For that's what one should come to expect,
Of a love affair with 'La Lune.'

Karen Jarman (16)
St Paul's RC School, Leicester

DRACULA

As I looked out on Hallowe'en night,
I saw a man in a cape who gave me a fright.
He was standing on the top of the old church tower,
Then he turned round, saw me and gave me a glower.
As quick as a lightning bolt he turned into a bat
And flew into the night, how about that!
Then on great silent wings the bat sped by
And I saw it silhouetted against the moon in the sky.
I remembered the scary film I had seen the night before
And all at once there came a knock at the door!
Assuming it was Dracula I was reluctant at first,
He might be looking to quench his foul thirst!
I opened the door and to my relief I found,
Just a group of children messing around!
'Trick or treat!'
I handed out sweets and chocolates galore
And then I finally shut the door.
I didn't encounter the man in the cape,
I'm thankful I had a lucky escape!

Katherine Gwilliam (11)
St Paul's RC School, Leicester

I Am Lost

I am;
a sock
lost in a washing machine
by my owner
I'm keen to be found
it's very
mean that I'm not.

I am;
a page
torn from a book
a missing chapter of a story
lost since The Iron Age
no one will look at.

Callum Wright (12)
St Paul's RC School, Leicester

December

From a dark December evening
As a sharp frost bites
To a bright December morning
Filled with frosty delights
Although our world is colder
And the summer sun is past
Christmas time is coming
So we want this time to last
As advent passes slowly
Though we pray for this to go
The tense wait for Santa
Now begins to show.

Joseph Garfield (12)
St Paul's RC School, Leicester

MY POEM

My favourite hobby is listening to music,
Whether listening to it a lot or just a bit
It is guaranteed to be a great hit,
My favourite singers are Eminem and Britney Spears
But whoever it is I'm always the first to hear.

My favourite types of music are;
R 'n' B, dance and hip hop.
But the best is of course pop,
I listen to the charts every week with no delay,
But if something comes up I read it in the paper
The next day.

And that's why I love music because it makes me feel happy.

Fiona Rodrigues (11)
St Paul's RC School, Leicester

AUTUMN

Autumn leaves are falling down,
Closing in all around,
Winter is drawing near
And hibernating creatures fear,
Winter is nearly here.

Crispy yellow, crimson and gold,
Autumn brings frost and cold,
Spring is next, it brings new life,
It's time for males to find a wife.

Autumn leaves are falling down,
Closing in all around.

Amy Barker (13)
St Paul's RC School, Leicester

I Am Tasty

I am
  A lime
  Tangy but smooth
  If you like me
  You have a sweet tooth
  Sometimes I'm sour
  Sometimes I'm not
  It depends how you're feeling
  Cold or hot.

        I am
          A wedding cake
          I am precious
          If someone dropped me
          They'd be turned into ashes
          Lots of care and work
          Has gone into me
          To make someone's day very happy.

I am
  Wine
  With which people like to dine
  I am drank with spuds or beans
  But at the end of the day
  I know what it means
  I am luscious
  Irresistibly tasty
  When you wake up in the morning
  Your head will be aching.

Nathalie Shearer (12)
St Paul's RC School, Leicester

APRIL

26th April is my birthday
It's like sitting in fresh hay
Blossom all around
Floating to the ground

Little lambs being born
Then the fields full of corn
Easter eggs everywhere
All the trees no longer bare

Frost is lying on the ground
A crispy, crunchy, crackling sound
Shoots appearing in the mud
Plenty of flowers out in bud

The sun is higher in the sky
Flocks of geese flying by
Daffodils turn their golden heads
While other flowers come out their beds

Baby calves and foals abound
In the meadows all around
Farmers busy in the field
Making sure of a harvest yield

April is a month of joy
For every little girl and boy
It heralds, yes the start of spring
To every single living thing.

Emily Stevens (12)
St Paul's RC School, Leicester

IN THIS WONDERFUL MAY

May's the time for plants to bloom
The blossoming trees are bowery
Below plants grow in gloom
Now it's not so showery
In this wonderful May

May is at the end of spring
It's the fifth month of the year
When the birds in the trees sing
It almost brings a tear
In this wonderful May

May is a rainbow at the end of a storm
Now that it's stopped pouring
The warm sun begins to form
Hibernated animals stop their snoring
In this wonderful May

May is the time to be at the park
After the grass has had its mow
And stay there till it gets dark
Now that it's not going to snow
In this wonderful May

May is the time to have a spring clean
Tidy, dust, iron and wash the pan
Everyone helps and works as a team
It will be spik and span
In this wonderful May

May is the finest month of spring
Fruits may make a surprise appearance
A gift that Mother Nature brings
Underneath all this garden clearance
In this wonderful May.

Chris Bates (12)
St Paul's RC School, Leicester

RIDING

Nervous, breathlessly waiting,
I see a horse
It's not for me
But the anticipation grows
And I get a funny feeling in my tummy.

A jet-black horse
With big broad shoulders
Although not as tall as the rest
She calls me over
I'm really nervous.

My hands are quivering like leaves
I stumble over, then clamber up
My horse walks to the water
Bumping me up and down as he goes.

He has a drink then sneezes
I'm shocked and cling on
Grabbing the saddle tightly
I become more confident and relax my grip
The feeling in my tummy slowly disappearing.

We start to walk out the gate
And then begin to trot
My heart pounds with excitement
As we make our way
Steadily up the road.

I feel the hot sun on my back
We stop for a moment
For others to catch up
My horse jerks its head down to eat
Almost pulling me over its head.

Ashley Fraine (14)
St Paul's RC School, Leicester

EXILED TO ENGLAND

Stranded and dejected
I stand alone.
An outsider, a refugee.
First betrayed, then marooned
On this island.
Forsaken and friendless,
A sad soul to see.

How quiet and reserved,
Aloof and remote,
Our reclusive new neighbour
Seems to be.
We welcomed him here,
Not ostracised or shunned
The forlorn exiled stranger.

Passing ships
Have tried to land and reach out to me,
They see I am pathetic and piteous.
This miserable, melancholy mood
Isolates me.
Abandoned, alone,
Away from my native country.

Rebecca Murphy (16)
St Paul's RC School, Leicester

THE SIMPSONS

Homer Simpson is great for a laugh,
He doesn't have enough brains to draw a graph.
His employer is Mr Burns,
Homer sleeps while he earns.

Lisa Simpson plays the saxophone,
She got caught talking to Cory on the telephone,
Bart Simpson is a natural troublemaker,
He's not a giver, he is a taker.

Simon Canty (12)
St Paul's RC School, Leicester

USELESSNESS

Sometimes I look at my life and I wonder
Is it worth it? I often blunder
In what I've done and what I'm doing
I still can't decide where I'm going.

I'm stuck with four A-Levels and two jobs
No proper friends - I hang round in mobs
I had a girlfriend but now she's left me
My work load at the moment is far too hefty.

It seems like nothing's going right
Sometimes my chest just feels so tight
I want to let it out and tell someone
But I'm scared that they'll just make fun.

My bike is broken, my bag is busted
I feel like them and I'm disgusted
And just last week my goldfish died
I've decided I'm going to commit suicide.

Don't ring the Samaritans, it's only a poem
I've got a lot of friends, I really know 'em
They would listen to me if I couldn't stick it
You see, my problem is I'm too melodramatic.

Thomas Eccles (16)
St Paul's RC School, Leicester

THE GRANGE!

There's a big old house,
But now there lives a mouse,
Under a bridge,
In an old village.

I entered inside,
Then guess what I spied,
A spider's web,
Made from wool and thread.

Outside rain was falling,
The cold wind began to moan,
The old house was squeaky and creaky,
With a ghostly moan.

The house was called 'The Grange',
I felt trapped when in the hall,
Then something strange,
Came floating from the wall.

Then I touched the wall,
And felt a chill,
Something began to crawl,
At its own will.

A ghost I spied,
From the picture inside,
There was standing a lady in white,
Who gave me such a fright?

Joanna Poleszczuk (13)
St Paul's RC School, Leicester

WHEN I LEAVE SCHOOL

The world is just an oyster,
People always say.
New York to San Francisco,
That's how I'll spend my day.

I'll work undercover for the FBI,
MI6 or MI5.
Then pilot a jet fighter flying over Europe,
Turning and swirling, trying to stay alive.

I'll ride a camel through Asia
And test gadgets in Japan,
Investigate Australia,
Then sail back to Milan.

I'll sky dive over Canada
And chase tornadoes in the Keys.
Canoe down the Mississippi
And conquer the seven seas.

I'll present the famous Oscars,
Shake hands with all the stars.
Meet the world's geniuses
And test the brand new cars.

All these things I'll try and do,
Maybe more if poss.
But first I'll have to finish school,
Then figure out the cost.

Anne-Marie Liszczyk (13)
St Paul's RC School, Leicester

FRIGHTENED I AMS

I am;
A frightened dog
Barking in the night.
A worried mouse
Shivering with fright.
A terrified tree
Being cut down.
A scary book
Frightening a clown.

I am;
A petrified rat
Being chased by a cat.
A frightened log
Being chewed by a dog.
A worried beetle
Being stamped on by a foot.
A haunted house
Where in the ghosts are put.

I am;
A terrible exam room
Where many meet their doom.
A spine-chilling bedroom
As cold as a tomb.
A graveyard at night
Ghosts ready to bite
A lion's prey
Running away.

Mary Frances van Kroonenburg (12)
St Paul's RC School, Leicester

THE OUTSIDE WORLD

*(This poem is about a child that gets beaten at home and locked
in a dark room with no light and no way of escape.)*

As the wind blows on this bleak, cold day,
He sits alone,
Isolated from the world,
Nobody to see his feelings never shown,
Feeling neglected, all alone.
As the sun shines still he sits,
Unloved and frightened,
Thinking of a way to reach the outside world.
No family, no friends,
Seeking treasure,
The outside world.
He begins to cry, thoughts screaming through his mind,
The door bolted shut from the opposite side,
No where to run, no where to hide.
Bruises on his body, covered in pain,
Trying to stay calm,
Trying to stay sane.
His life's never been happy, memories all sad,
All because of his parents,
His mum, his dad.
Imagining a perfect life,
Something this child's never had.
If only we could help children like these,
To make them feel loved, to care for their needs,
But we'll never stop this pain, this cruelty and abuse,
To give them a happy life to which they're not used.

Leah Pedge (13)
St Paul's RC School, Leicester

I HEAR

I hear the crowd roaring,
I hear the teams preparing,
I hear the mangers pep talk,
I hear the referee's whistle.

I hear the crowd chanting,
I hear the skipper encouraging,
I hear the manger instructing,
I hear the harsh tackles.

I hear the referee scolding,
I hear the excitement of the first goal,
I hear the half-time screams,
I hear the intercom chattering away.

I hear the tunnel come alight with grinding metal,
I hear the crowd cheer on the players,
I hear the referee restart the game,
I hear the players shout and swear.

I hear the appeal from in the area,
I hear the ball hit the net,
I hear the last gasp rally,
I hear the stunning winner.

I hear the final whistle,
I hear the rowdy supporters brag,
I hear the losers boo.

Feargal Brennan (11)
St Paul's RC School, Leicester

SPACE

When I look up to the stars,
I wonder what it's like
To be a floating astronaut
Where day turns into night?

I wonder how it feels?
I wonder what they think?
I wonder what they're going through
On their journey to the brink?

As they travel past asteroids,
Going to the moon
They are only metres away
From hurtling to their doom.

I see them on the tele,
I hear them on the news
As reporters fight for a quote
To represent their views.

I wonder what it's like
To see what they've all seen?
I wonder if I'll ever go,
Where Buzz and Neil have been?

I wish I was an astronaut,
Flying through the sky,
I wish I could explore the planets,
I wish the time was nigh.

Brendan Archdeacon (13)
St Paul's RC School, Leicester

THE PHOTO

It's the kind of photo
Which,
After three months of them being gone
You have to force yourself to look at.

Dusty around the edges,
Faded,
With finger marks, so
Touchable,
But embarrassing because it
Forces emotions.

'Eyes are the windows to the soul'
They say,
I say 'Eyes lie'
Perfectly matched,
Staring backs, arms gently
Around the shoulders.

Then
A brick wall. No attachment
Teeth biting behind the smiles,
And afterwards,
You remember
What you meant to say
When you had the chance.

Alissa Ruane (16)
St Paul's RC School, Leicester

FEAR

A small body running across the floor.
Creeping really quietly, quickly past the door.
A little hairy animal standing on its web.
Standing still not moving an inch
Pretending it was dead.

Smelling death smelling fear.
Ever so scared I won't go near.
Its hairy little body trying to creep up my skin.
If I was in a running race I'm sure that I would win.

Nathan Modeste (12)
St Paul's RC School, Leicester

BORING I AMS

I am;
Feeling like a normal worm
I just eat soil and I squirm
I am a person who likes very hard work
People think I'm a boring jerk.

I am;
An eel
We all do the same thing every day
During our life we breed then die,
We don't ask why
We've just got into the habit of live, breed and die.

I am;
A play of William Shakespeare's,
That nobody wants to read or even hear,
A sloth who just eats and sleeps all week,
I'm so bored I think I'll go to sleep.

I am;
A soap on TV,
Called Eastenders
Many people watch me,
My actors are horrendous,
My plots aren't real
And that it wouldn't take Holmes to reveal.

Christian Wheeliker (12)
St Paul's RC School, Leicester

COLD I AMS

I am;
The snowball in a snowball fight
Everyone is shivering
All around is glistening white
Even the trees are quivering!

I am;
Exploring the North Pole
Where everything is chilly
Into the sea some penguins roll
But the others are acting silly!

I am;
A tub of ice-cream
Just come out of the freezer
My flavour is whatever you dream
Strawberry, vanilla or Malteser!

I am;
A soft snowflake
Gently falling to the ground
White as the icing on a cake
Whirling, whirling, down and down!

I am;
Jack Frost beware
I creep about at night
Leaving patterns here and there
What a wonderful sight!

Josephine Hunt (12)
St Paul's RC School, Leicester

I AM QUIET

I am;
Like a quiet person
In an assembly with the amount
Of people in Wembley.

I am;
A sneaky and sheepy person
Like acting in a James Bond film
Trying to get to lessons without
Teachers seeing me as I'm late.

I am;
A very shaky person as I sit
In my test wondering how long's
Left and having little rests.

I am;
A very tired person as I get home
From school and I sit like a
Statue at the TV like a
Mummy saying I'm coming to get you.

I am;
Very sleepy as I crawl into my bed
Tired and shattered like I have
Just got beaten up as I faintly
Shut my eyes, goodbye!

Louis Lord (12)
St Paul's RC School, Leicester

WHAT DOES CHRISTMAS REALLY MEAN?

What does Christmas mean to some
Eating turkey, drinking rum?

But shouldn't it be about the star so bright
The birth of Jesus on a starry night?

But there's those who spend their time
Late night parties, drinking wine

But shouldn't it be about three wise men
Shepherds, angels in Bethlehem?

Mistletoe, mince pies, being too greedy
Shouldn't we be able to help the needy?

Shouldn't we think of the holy day
In a manger the baby lay?

Have time to think of Christmas Day
Of the baby Jesus lying in the hay.

Hannah Goodman (11)
St Paul's RC School, Leicester

UNTITLED

Created in dust
Shattered by light,
He leaves in the day
And returns at night.

The overrun squat
Is disposed of through the back,
Over the fields
Where people leave their track.

Coping with the sites
Is hard to keep strong,
It's just a shelter
But to him, staying seems wrong.

Created in dust
Shattered by light,
He leaves in the day
And returns at night.

Joe Lee (14)
St Paul's RC School, Leicester

FEAR OF FIRE!

Dark grey fumes,
Smouldering paper,
A gas cooker alight!

A crackling noise,
As blaring as thunder,
The red, orange and yellow wisps spiral.

A burning scent,
A wisp of fumes
Covering the air.

Hot burning heat,
Then shivering
Down my spine.

A foul taste of
Burning smoke,
A deadly sign.

Kathryn Drake (12)
St Paul's RC School, Leicester

Happy I Ams

I am
the crashing waves of the sea
the first slice of cake you see.

I am
the beach, all the shells and pebbles are
within my reach.

I am
the present that can walk, no other
present can walk or talk.

I am
a trip that takes you out for the day
you do not have to pay.

I am
the new car to take you out and about
I will not let you down without a doubt.

I am
the cake that you eat off a plate
I will also get you in a state.

I am
the boat that keeps you afloat when sailing
on the sea
and when the waves go crashing you will all shout with glee.

I am
the car all shiny and new, that you bought from
the showroom in a town called Crewe.
my paintwork is gleaming, no doubt you will be screaming.

Rebecca Cooper (12)
St Paul's RC School, Leicester

THE BEACH

When I go to the beach on a hot sunny day,
I hear children scream and shout as they play.

I hear the sea rolling in and out
Shifting the sand all about.

I hear the seagulls flying in the sky
As they flutter gracefully by.

Then I hear people chant, 'It's lunch, it's lunch'
And as they get out their lunch I hear, 'Munch, munch, munch.'

I hear the grown-ups chatting away,
Talking about their great holiday.

I hear dogs barking and running about
Jumping into the sea and then dashing out.

When I go to the beach on a cold windy day
I don't hear any children shouting, 'Let's play, let's play.'

Instead I hear the tide crashing up against the shore,
One wave, two wave, three wave four.

I hear children throwing pebbles into the sea,
Splish, splish, 'Bet you can't throw further than me?'

I hear the wind flying ferociously by,
Lifting old chip wrappers high into the sky.

I hear people shivering and saying in dismay,
'I do hope tomorrow's a far better day.'

I hear boat sails rattling and blowing about,
Far too windy for sailors to take them out.

Rachel Doyle (11)
St Paul's RC School, Leicester

SWIMMING

Swimming through the water
Like a little fish,
Staying in the pool forever,
I wish!
The refreshing water splashing against my
face,
Sometimes I like swimming in a race,
Splashing in the water
Splashing all around,
When I'm underwater I can't hear a sound,
Swimming really fast,
Swimming really slow,
I have to finish off now
It's nearly time to go.

Lucy Birch (11)
St Paul's RC School, Leicester

FOOTBALL!

Football crazy, football mad,
It could be happy, it could be sad.
The whistle blows, the players call,
They all want to kick the ball.
The linesman flags, the player frowns.
He shouts, 'That player was pushed down!'
The crowd are cheering for the free kick,
The wall has worked, like a brick,
His head attacks the ball with flair,
You see it fly into the hole
The players shout
Goal! Goal! Goal!

Ashley Robinson (11)
St Paul's RC School, Leicester

MY FEAR

The slimy, slithery, long animal.
It moves slowly through the long, thick grass
Its scaly skin runs across the floor.
Its frightful look could break a glass.

The rattle vibrates like a happy baby.
The hiss is creepy and gives me the shivers.
The scream of a human when they're squeezed to death
Gives me a funny feeling in my livers.

The smell of a dead mouse from its breath
The smell of a dead bird devoured by it
Worst of all the ugly sights
Of a dad man lying after being bit.

Chibuzor Chilaka (12)
St Paul's RC School, Leicester

FOOTBALL

As I tied up my boots
And put on my shirt
The colours of victory
Let out a roar!
The fans were singing,
The whistle blew,
Win, lose or draw,
I know I must score.
My heart was beating,
As I pulled back my leg
I thundered the ball
To the back of the net.

Piero Cossu (11)
St Paul's RC School, Leicester

COLD I AMS

Cold I ams

Of the wind around my feet,
My toes need some heat.
I can hardly walk.
I'm hungry and cold,
And I feel really old.
It's starting to rain,
As I walk down the lane.
And I start to wonder,
Will it really thunder?
It's raining harder now,
As I wipe the water from my brow.
Oh no, not lightning,
I find that really frightening.
Is that a light I see up ahead?
All I dream of is my bed.
My feet and hands feel like ice,
I can't wait to feel warm and nice.
My joints are so stiff,
I really need a lift.
At last here is a car,
That man is a star.
The heater is on fast,
I am warm at last.

Danielle Newcombe (13)
St Paul's RC School, Leicester

TRAVELLING DAN

Travelling Dan, travelling Dan
He don't stay long he's a travelling man
He travels on a bus, and he travels on a train
As soon as he arrives he's a travelling again

Travelling Dan, travelling Dan
He drives all day in his travelling van
He drives through the country, he drives through the town
He drives all day till his battery wears down.

Sean McGlone (13)
St Paul's RC School, Leicester

I HEAR

At the disco I hear,
loud thumping music,
and people singing along noisily
I hear feet banging rowdily,
as people dance and walk in heeled shoes,
I hear the DJ booming out song titles,
and people laughing and shouting,
I hear mobile phones ringing
and people promising Mum they'll be home by nine.
I hear change dropping into the tin,
as refreshments are brought.
I can hear the electric humming,
so softly the quietist noise in the room.
I hear glass shatter,
as drinks are accidentally dropped.
I hear the clock strike ten
and the screams of those supposed to be home by nine,
I hear the double doors bang,
as people start to leave.
I hear my friends say 'Goodbye'
as I myself step outside.
I'm outside, I hear quiet giggling over the road
and the clatter of feet walking to houses, taxis and bus stops
and then the party is over and I hear nothing.

Natasha Fraine (12)
St Paul's RC School, Leicester

THE BEACH

I hear,
the chattering of the people
as they gather on the beach,
the voice of the deck chair man
is close within our reach,
'Two chairs and a brolly - just
a pound or two'
mum and dad both sit down
but I would like one too!
An extra chair soon arrives
this one's just for me,
I fetch my bucket and my spade
and head towards the sea.
But then I hear the ice cream man
shouting up the beach,
'Vanilla cone or strawberry
raspberry or peach?'
Chocolate is my favourite
I hope he's got some too,
but if he hasn't got that flavour
I haven't got a clue!
The man is selling drinks now
and mum and dad can hear,
'Cola, Cola, Fanta, Fanta,
Lemonade or beer.'
It's time for us to go now
I hear the seagulls in the sky,
the day is nearly over
as the ferry boat goes by.

Paul Knight (11)
St Paul's RC School, Leicester

BOASTFUL I AMS

I am,

    Peaches,

I am,

    Cream.

I am,

    The captain of the team.
    I'll be your mate,
    Because . . .

I am,

    So great!
    You'll love me,
    Because I have lots of money.
    I will be king one day,
    I know I will.
    Do you like me yet?
    I think you will!

I am,

    Fast and I have a Dreamcast.
    I have all the latest games!
    By the way, what's your name?
    I'll go to the moon,
    I hope quite soon.

I am,

    The cleverest in my class!
    I've already passed my GCSEs!
    I'll fight anyone,
    Leave them begging on their knees!
    So go on be my mate,
    Because . . .

I am,

    So great!

Sam Hill (12)
St Paul's RC School, Leicester

MY FEAR

The cool, steel glint,
The waiting, the tension,
The slow walk of the nurse,
The smell of antiseptic.
No smile just a glum face
As sharp as the blade.
She comes towards me now
And shaking like a leaf I speak
And ask if it'll hurt. I know it will.
The pointy blade,
The cold glare of the nurse.
I feel queasy, and now the chime
Of the clock is louder than usual.
Now she rests the needle on my arm,
Presses, pushes I can feel it pierce my skin,
I can hear my own scream,
I can hear the nurse say it's all over.
I can hardly move as frozen as stiff
As the needle, but still
I push myself up towards the door,
And as I do that the nurse's
Long, cold fingers slide towards
My jacket and press a sticker on it.
Well done. That's what it says.

Carolyn Kelly (12)
St Paul's RC School, Leicester

FEAR

I see black things rushing
across the floor at night.
It's creepy, hairy and has many legs,
when it makes its web to trap his prey,
it watches you 'til it's ready to strike.

When its hairy legs get on you
it tingles your skin, then makes you
shiver from head to toe.
When it bites, it stings
like a knife going into you.

Elroy Silcott (13)
St Paul's RC School, Leicester

MY FRIEND THE MONSTER

My friend the monster
Is such a dude
He's so cool
But he's so rude

My friend the monster
Is only five foot four
Which is really useful
When walking through a door

My friend the monster
Has a green face
He's fat and ugly
But he can win any race

My friend the monster
He is a noisy fellow
He snorts and he growls
He screeches and he bellows

My friend the monster
Isn't really fancied
The reason's quite simple
He smells rather rancid.

Rebecca Boynton (11)
St Paul's RC School, Leicester

MONEY

Money is such an important thing
We cannot live without it
It's a bit like life itself
Small change as important as the pounds
It can buy all manner of wonderful things
And that was just the half of it
Money is everything
I couldn't live without it.
But there is one thing that money can't buy
And that's friendship.

There is a downside to money though
As you either have to work hard to earn it
Or you inherit it or get it as a present
There are also bills
And debts to pay off
Some people don't have enough,
Some people have too much.
But there is one thing that money can't buy
And that's friendship.

John Taylor (11)
St Paul's RC School, Leicester

I HEAR

People cheering as the players come out,
They come out of the tunnel for a run about,
The sound of the whistle starts the match and the
Goalie makes the first good catch.

Half-time comes and burgers are sold
Everyone buys them because they're freezing cold.

Steve Waldrom (11)
St Paul's RC School, Leicester

THE DREADED GHOST SHIP

Every night there is a whistling in my ears,
It is coming from the dreaded ghost ship,
Sailing in the clouds.
Every night it comes from the moon,
Firing its silent cannons in my ears.
Its captain is a flying pig,
With wings made of bone.
His eyes are the colour of boiled blood
And swirls of dancing fire.
He makes his slaves push the enormous cannons
Till they drop unconscious on the deck.
In the morning it sails away,
Back to the moon,
Lands in a colossal crater
And stays there . . .
Until the next dreaded haunting!

Adam Thuraisingam (11)
St Paul's RC School, Leicester

A ROAD IS LIKE . . .

A road is like
A river of black,
With private yachts
Carrying one or two
Ferries carrying
Thirty passengers
And huge great
Cargo ships
Monsters of the sea.

Natalie Lisiewicz (13)
St Paul's RC School, Leicester

THE BOY CALLED SEAN

One day Sean was walking along singing a groovy song
He'd heard it that morning on Radio One.
He scuffed his feet in the snowy ground.
Sean bent over, what had he found? It was a ten pound.
He arrived at the bookies he'd ran all the way.
I'll put ten pound on Goldbelt, he just managed to say.
'It's five million to one you know' the man said.
'I really don't care' Sean said 'I'll prove I'm not off my head.'
After many nail-biting minutes finally Goldbelt won.
Everyone was shocked, they called for a dope test to be done.
'What can I do with the money' Sean thought
A quick think and presents for all the family he'd bought.
When he got home his brother went as white as snow.
He said 'I'll kill you if you're lying you know.'
His mother opened a bottle of expensive wine.
His dad nailed up a 'For Sale' sign.
Poor old Sean went betting again,
He put the lot on a 20-1 called Seany Ben.
And guess what he lost the lot.
                    Not!

Anthony Bales (11)
St Paul's RC School, Leicester

SNAKES AND LADDERS

It's snakes' delight to hiss and bite
And little mice to squeak
And if you climb Mount Everest
You'll finally reach the peak.

David Sewell (11)
St Paul's RC School, Leicester

CAKES!

Cakes I like to eat are
Chocolate cakes, jam cakes,
Cream cakes, sponge cakes
Any cakes - every cakes
That you could make.

Cakes I bake are great
To taste, mixing and stirring,
Tasting and slurping
- Sorry Mum I'm burping!
Making the icing - sugary and sweet.
My jeans are bursting
This icing is neat!

The cake events are
Christmas, birthdays, Easter and Sundays
Oh what fun days
But how I hate Mondays
- Cos then it's
Washing-up day!

Rachael Jones (11)
St Paul's RC School, Leicester

FEAR

It just sits in the corner and stares
When you're in bed it runs around upstairs.
When you wake up you see it and you're scared
Its eight hairy legs tickle you if it touches you.
You try and catch it but it runs to its lair
It runs over your lap but it has no care.

Gemma Mills (12)
St Paul's RC School, Leicester

DANGEROUS ANIMALS

A crocodile has dangerously
Sharp teeth
But it's so scary
I'm going to be very brief.
A tiger can rip you to shreds
In a minute
His tummy will rumble
Thirty seconds after you're in it,
A hawk can pull your eyes out
With its claws
They are as sharp as forty saws,
A wasp can give you very bad stings
Wasps have very noisy wings.
A bull is fast at charging
The people in the stadium with them must
Be good at dodging
But the most breathtaking of all
Is the big, strong, hairy and tall
No it's not a caterpillar it's a
Gorilla!

Joseph Fallon (11)
St Paul's RC School, Leicester

WINTER

Season of sleep and glistening snow
Coldness wrapping like a blanket
Icy fingers caressing the landscape
The frost, suffocating the remaining flowers.

Gone is the season of colour
The greys obliterate the landscape
Covering everything in bleakness
The howls echo through the night.

Frozen is time in this world of shadows
The rains attack in armies
The winds, relentless in their punishment of the barren trees
Strip them of their dignity.

Winter, his frozen hand the solitary comfort
As those who sleep
Look forward to seeing bursts of colour,
Spring.

Michelle Newcombe (16)
St Paul's RC School, Leicester

SMELLY

Going for a run
Is a lot of fun.

Although it makes me hot
It's the best hobby I've got.

I like to run and think
But it really makes me stink.

And I no longer smell of flowers
I shall need at least two showers.

The water is cold
But I still smell pretty old.

I'll have another shower
Now I will smell like a flower.

So I will go to bed
To rest my weary head.

Declan Weston (11)
St Paul's RC School, Leicester

POEM OF . . . ?

I see something,
What could it be?
It just sits in the corner and
Stares at me,
It has eight scary legs,
Two beady eyes,
It runs around everywhere,
And often loves the big flies,
On my knee, on my lap,
And places itself on my colourful cap,
When you're in bed,
It climbs up the wall and you wonder
Where it will fall,
You start to scream,
You try to catch it,
Oh dear it's fallen into the cream,
I hate the black hairy creatures and
Certainly their hairy features.

Krystyna Frost (12)
St Paul's RC School, Leicester

THE LION

A great big lion you do see

A great big lion looking at me
He'll give me a meal
Yes for free
That's a great deal
Don't you agree?

Sapphia Cunningham-Tate (11)
St Paul's RC School, Leicester

ABBIE DABBIE

I've got a baby sister called Abbie,
Who likes to scream and play,
If you make her laugh,
She will have a laughing fit.
If you're down in the dumps,
Here's Abbie the life saver,
That makes you laugh and play, all day,
She's small, funny and bubbly,
And sometimes if she feels like it, cuddly,
She runs around like mad,
And screams if she can.
She's a lively wee thing,
She's precious to me,
She doesn't care what anyone looks like,
She's a friend to everyone,
I love and adore her,
So much!

Lisa Bungart (11)
St Paul's RC School, Leicester

SWIMMING

As I walk up to the pool
I feel so cool
The feeling of swimming makes me drool
As I jump into the pool
The water's so cool
As cold as ice
It feels so nice
I have much fun
Until it's time to run.

Luigi Manzione (11)
St Paul's RC School, Leicester

MANCHESTER UNITED

M ark Bosnich!
A rsenal watch out!
N aughty tackles,
C ross managers,
H ate the ref.
E ric Cantona!
S ent off
T iming wrong
E xtra time
R yan Giggs!

U mbro
N ear the post
I n the goal
T eddy Sheringham!
E xcited fans
D avid Beckham scored!

Kazminder Sangha (11)
St Paul's RC School, Leicester

MY BEST FRIEND

She's like a fiery flower,
Bright and colourful with reds and yellows,
She's loud and cheerful, always happy,
She's also like a hot summer's day, very warm,
Without cold snow she's as bright as the sun,
Like a jewel in a crown can never be missed,
Walking around with a smile so bright,
She makes everyone happy,
She loves to be right.

Francesca A Del Core (11)
St Paul's RC School, Leicester

THE DEVIL'S DAUGHTER

There's a beautiful mermaid
With blue crystals round her neck
Just like her eyes
She has turquoise scales
Glistening in the clear blue sea
Her lips are like ice cubes
Of course she looks nice
But at night she's a red hot spice
Her crystals are fire
Her scales are blinding red
Her lips are like an iron
But covered in venom
She goes round the mermaid's palace
And tortures the king and queen
While her slaves steal the gold
She is the Devil's daughter.

Catherine Wilkins (11)
St Paul's RC School, Leicester

MAGICIANS

Magicians you see on a stage
Ask for any people of any age
Volunteers in a box
Rabbits out of a hat
And volunteers go through a door
Abracadabra, fiddle faddle
You will now disappear
Victims in a basket
Magician doing the magic
Audience stunned!

Neeraj Parmar (11)
St Paul's RC School, Leicester

THE GHOST

I see a ghost wearing black,
I see the ghost with no head,
I see the ghost standing tall,
I see its shadow in the hall,
I see the ghost near by bed,
I feel a shiver down my spine,
I feel as if I'm going to die,
I feel as if I want to cry,
I feel like it is a lie
I feel as if I'm not alive,
I hear the howling in the wind,
I hear the ghost whisper me,
I hear it screeching at my bed,
I hear the strike of twelve o'clock,
I hear, I feel, I see nothing.

Daniel McMurray (11)
St Paul's RC School, Leicester

MY MILLENNIUM VIEW

The year 2000 will be upon us soon,
Celebrations, parties, crowds and balloons.
The Millennium Dome is as big as the moon,
I hope the Dome is ready soon.
As time goes by the years role on
Another century is soon gone.
The Millennium Bug as dangerous as a bear,
So I tell you *beware! Beware!*
The Millennium year will be here soon
It wildly pounces on us soon like a *big* baboon.
Good luck Millennium!

Paul Watts (11)
St Paul's RC School, Leicester

ROLLER-COASTER

I see a dark ride, fast as a slide,
Round, round and upside down,
Twirling round, whizzing, spinning
It's so fast how long will it last?
I hear a screaming sound,
The cracking of the ride,
Someone's crying as though someone has died
It smells of sick
I really want to get off quick.
It smells of oil
Worse than freshly mixed soil,
I taste the candyfloss and the popcorn
As it goes all over my friend Siobhan.
I wish I hadn't been to this fair,
Because it's been a real scare.

Kathleen Durkan (12)
St Paul's RC School, Leicester

ME AND MY BEST FRIEND . . .

Me and my best friend have been
friends for eight years,
We had a few fights, and shared laughter
and tears.

Shared lots of secrets and cute little pets,
We've been to Yarmouth together but not abroad yet.

We've slept round each other's house,
And been scared by a mouse.
I'll see you soon because I'm going to go now,
I think I'll sign off and take a big bow.

Rhia Tansey (11)
St Paul's RC School, Leicester

STAR WARS

Star Wars was made a movie twenty-two years ago,
R2D2 was a robot and so was C3P0,
Luke learned to be a Jedi knight Yoda taught him how,
Han Solo was a smuggler but joined the rebel crowd.
Then they made episode one which was cool.
Darth Maul was a Sith Lord,
Anakin was a slave,
Amidala pretended to be Padme,
C3P0 was half made,
Obi Wan was a younger great Jedi knight,
He used his lightsaber for protection in all his courageous fights.
Overall in Star Wars I'm their biggest fan
I've seen all their movies they're really fab
Star Wars is fun for everyone and I think
You should watch them too.

Michael Fowler (11)
St Paul's RC School, Leicester

STARGAZER

Ruby orb-eyed, spearheaded ears,
White as Arctic driven snow,
Cotton bud tailed.
Sharp, alert, aware,
Leaping, darting, evading
Suddenly he freezes.
He is motionless, twitching, searching,
Still as a statue.
He is the king of his kind,
He is Stargazer.

Lucy Bryant (11)
St Paul's RC School, Leicester

THE TWO MALICIOUS MONSTERS

Once two malicious monsters
as big as the seconds in an era
came down from their purpose in the sky
and battled it out to the end

The battle was arranged centuries ago
and to the winner Heaven will be close
and Hell even further away

The creatures - like unstoppable lies
fought as ongoing as time
their faces so focused
like someone seeing an amazing sight

In the end the cunning won
with brains as strong as steel.

Adam Brown (11)
St Paul's RC School, Leicester

THAT'S A MYSTERY

I hate school, it's easy to see,
Anyone who likes it that's a mystery.
With tests in grammar and all
I'm personally appalled.

I hate school, it's easy to see,
Anyone who likes it that's a mystery.
With push and shove in the hall -
Five broken fingers overall.

But in the end school isn't that bad;
Because not *all* the teachers get mad.

Patrick Mendes (11)
St Paul's RC School, Leicester

THE RUGBY WORLD CUP

R   ugby, rugby everywhere
U   ruguay, France, Spain and the Spring Boks too
'G   o on England,' chant the English fans
B   rilliant players like Jonah Lomu
Y   ellow, black and white shirts

W   ow! All the colour and all the excitement
O   ur team is losing what a big dilemma
R   ats! He's missed the penalty, oh no!
L   ook now he's running down the line
D   ebacle he's been tackled but it was far too high

C   lap, clap go the crowd as the players come off
U   'ave won the bet my friend I
P   lace the money in your 'and.

Luke Hawker (12)
St Paul's RC School, Leicester

CATS

Crawling around the house
Trying so hard to catch a mouse,
Trying his best to go through the flap,
I call 'Puss, Puss' and he comes on my lap,
Near the fire on the mat,
I see a little pussy cat,
He's hungry now, he crawls to his bowl
But there's nothing there, poor old soul,
Yawn, he's tired now, he's going up the stairs,
But it's cold up there oh who cares,
Prr, prr, closing his eyes,
I can tell you one thing, cats never lie.

Christina Coyle (11)
St Paul's RC School, Leicester

THE NON-HUMAN

A slithering fiend
Feared by human beings.
As sharp as a bullet
It will put you in its gullet,
Its scaly skin
Is as dark as a dustbin,
With his very pointy claws
You should give him applause
And his serpentine skin
Very scaly and thin.
So be sure within
That you don't encounter this non-human being.

Scott Wightman (12)
St Paul's RC School, Leicester

THE GHOST IN THE NIGHT

One dark night
I saw a ghost
Over by a beaming lamppost
He floated up
Towards the sky
The scary sight
Made me want to cry
I ran inside!
And closed the door
So I couldn't
See it
Any more!

Christopher Hirrell (11)
St Paul's RC School, Leicester

THE HALLOWE'EN POEM

It's the 31st October again,
It's nearly wintertime,
Smell that spell,
Witches yell,
Broomsticks all around,
Cauldrons burn,
Pumpkins alight,
Ghosts forever white,
Trick or treating,
Central heating
Children are on their way,
The quiet nights,
Dark and spooky,
Oh how I wish it was never day.

Samantha Staskiewicz (12)
St Paul's RC School, Leicester

FOOTBALL

Played with a ball as round as a sphere,
Eleven players each as fit as a cheetah,
Goalkeepers as bouncy as kangaroos,
Defenders as strong as a skyscraper,
Midfielders as fast as Linford Christie,
Forwards as powerful as can be,
Managers with as many brains as a scientist,
Physios as knowledgeable as doctors,
Supporters as loyal as can be,
The chairman as confident as confidence can get
And there's a fan like me.

Frankie Monk (11)
St Paul's RC School, Leicester

CHOCOLATE

The best thing about chocolate,
It melts in your mouth.
It sticks to your teeth,
And it doesn't come out.

You can get all different dark and light,
And if you're lucky even white.
It's bubbly, foamy, sparkly and fizzy,
And when you eat lots it makes you go dizzy.

A Galaxy of chocolate is lovely and sweet,
And we only get it for a treat.
If you take a bite you know you'll have to eat the rest,
So now you know Galaxy is the best.

Lorna Grant (12)
St Paul's RC School, Leicester

MILLENNIUM

The millennium, the millennium,
It marks the birth of Christ,
When Jesus began his life.
2000 years and we still believe
That's why we're celebrating on New Year's Eve.
We're all getting ready
For this interesting date
So come along and celebrate
Make the day special and worth it too,
But remember why we're doing this,
For Jesus Christ our Lord;
Who we love, worship and adore.

Hannah Turner (11)
St Paul's RC School, Leicester

X

1 - 2 X is coming for you,
3 - 4 better lock your door,
5 - 6 get your crucifix,
7 - 8 don't stay up late,
Now who's afraid of the dark?
Responsible for the murders in the park,
Then hear the boom and feel the spark
And I see the part that used to be your head
Replaced by nothing.
With your back cut open and your legs cut off,
You must be tired of me,
My name is really funny,
X is coming for you!

Simon Castanha (11)
St Paul's RC School, Leicester

CATS

Big cats, small cats,
Fat cats, thin cats,
Poor cats, rich cats,
Different cats.

Biting, spitting,
Hissing, tricking,
Scheming, plotting,
Mad cats.

Licking, purring,
Curling, kneading,
Pawing, loving,
My cat.

Tom Burke (11)
St Paul's RC School, Leicester

ICE-CREAM

Pink, blue, green and yellow
If you ask you might get melon.
Chocolate sprinkles on the top
I'm not saying 'No' yet because I don't want to stop!
In a dish or in a cone
Either way I will not moan.
I've just been out to the shops
There's a new flavour it's called Brussels and Chops.
I've had some just today
It's lovely but what can I say?
It's ice-cream!
Mint, vanilla, chocolate too
Lemon and vodka topped off with Taboo.

Lucy Farrell (11)
St Paul's RC School, Leicester

FEAR

I see a hairy body running along the floor.
One second it's there, the next it's on the door.
With its narrow, beady eyes and eight long legs
I run upstairs and jump under my bed.

I see something small on the top stair.
It looks to me like there could be a pair.
To my horror, they start to move near.
So I get up, and put myself in gear.

I go to the corner and grab a swat
To live much longer? I think not.
I raise the swat and slap it on their head.
To live much longer? No they're dead.

Danielle Satchell (12)
St Paul's RC School, Leicester

IN THE MIND

A poet's imaginary beast,
Doesn't take shape until he has a feast,
On all the delicious words,
That help him to cast his web of magic.

His mind, creative, positive,
Artistic, original, imaginative,
His gruesome being is breathing its first breath,
Ready to cause many people . . . death!

Turning the world on its head,
Snatching poor children while in bed,
But do not worry, for this is only a few marks on paper,
For all it is, is an interesting caper.

Christopher Farrin (11)
St Paul's RC School, Leicester

SPORTS GO-CART

S peed
P erformance
O verdrive
R eality
T hrills
S licks

G eometry
O il

C hanting crowd
A ero dynamics
R acing
T ension in the brakes.

Robert Ziemelis (11)
St Paul's RC School, Leicester

THE MONSTERS FROM WOODLY PIER

It's cold outside in the night,
Wet and damp it's cold alright,
In the mist behind a cloud,
A monster appears to bellow loud,
People flee inside their homes
Afraid to exit out the zone

Rustle, rustle go the trees
The monsters are on the move *oh dear*

Scales on their bodies and head
This is the moment the villagers dread
Children are warm safe in their beds
This is what the monsters said!

Children, children never fear,
We're the monsters from Woodly Pier
People say we bellow loud
Echoing fear through the clouds
We would not hurt a single bone
On anyone living within this zone

In our throats live some frogs
We bellow loud to let them hop
They live here to keep safe and warm
And out of the wind the rain the storm

So never fear when here
The monsters bellowing from Woodly Pier
The frogs have got to have a hop
Around our mouths
Have you forgot?

Jessica Welsted (11)
St Paul's RC School, Leicester

DARK

Your heart begins to race,
It's difficult to breathe,
The blackness surrounds you,
Figures, shapes, disappear,
You're all alone.

Bumping,
Bashing, into objects,
Rummaging,
Moving slowly all around.
Creaking floorboards,
Footsteps deafening.

You smell a stench,
What could it be?
A mountain of food mangled together,
or . . .
A pile of half-eaten rubbish, scattered around the floor,
What could it be?

Moving your hand across a cold wall,
Trying to find a light switch,
You're totally alert,
A single sound makes you jumpy.

Breathing deeply,
Your body shaking,
Your eyes are blank,
You can't see a thing.

Emma Dawes (12)
St Paul's RC School, Leicester

I'VE SEEN A MONSTER

I've seen a monster
He lives in the sea
He's slimy and ugly
And as tall as a tree.

He munches on humans
With his sharp razor jaws
He stamps on passing fishes
With his huge, scaly paws.

This monster has got
The most hideous face
And if he roared
You would hear it in space.

His skin's slimy and scaly
His colour is green
He is gruesome and fierce
And really mean.

He likes it at night-time
But hates it in the day
He always likes buying things
But never likes to pay.

I'll tell you a secret
About this monster I know
He's not scared of anything
Except for a crow.

Charlotte Shutt (11)
St Paul's RC School, Leicester

RESPONSE FROM A COY MISTRESS

Thee has received Thy letter,
I have read through and have been informed,
The persuasion does not flatter,
The things that were said weren't churned.

'Though' what you said was not truthful,
You said to me I had time,
But in the end, our love shall be fruitful,
But will your love to me be a crime?

You want to lose my virginity for me,
Therefore I might or just will not,
There is one decision, will capture thee,
If you lovest me enough or not.

So what is your decision?
If thy's decision is bright,
Then it should concern some vision,
If it is bad let it see light.

Will you my sweet, be kind,
Therefore will you respect my emotions,
So make sure that I do not fall behind,
Will you be satisfied with my decision?

Alkesh Mistry (14)
Soar Valley College

BRUCE LEE

He is fast as a cheetah.
He is as sour as a raw lemon.
He is as dangerous as a 25,000 volt battery.
He is bright as a burning sun.

He is like a Venus flytrap.
As strong as a nuclear weapon.
As famous as a popstar.
He is always agile as a cat.

Nayan Chawala (13)
Soar Valley College

ARNOLD SCHWARZENEGGER

He is like a huge fridge
as loud as a machine-gun
as big as a door
he is always at war
he is strong as a monster truck
as strong as an engine
he is strong like a Rottweiler
he is like thunder
as fast as a motorbike
he is like a lion.

Ashish Dhorajiya (13)
Soar Valley College

STONE-COLD STEVE AUSTIN

He is a monster truck,
As strong as a wall,
As hard as a jaw-breaker,
He is as hot as chilli,
He is thunder and storm,
As big and bulky as a cupboard,
As wild as a flower,
He is a rattlesnake.

Rughvir Singh Sandhu (13)
Soar Valley College

RICKY MARTIN

He is like a big comfortable leather sofa.
As refreshing as a bath in the sea.
As sweet as a puppy.
When he blushes he goes red as a rose.
He is as posh as a limo.
He is spicy as Indian food.
He has a body like silk.

Priya Patel (13)
Soar Valley College

RYAN GIGGS

He is like a tornado,
As fast as a cheetah,
As powerful as a rocket,
He is always the greatest,
He scores solo runs,
As rough as a lion,
As flexible as a spring,
His goal against Arsenal will always be treasured.

Hitul Unadkat (13)
Soar Valley College

MY POEM ON CATHERINE ZETA JONES

She is a cat flexible and agile,
She is as beautiful as Paris.
She is like classical music, soft and sweet,
Her lips are as red as red rose.
She is like a warm summer's day,
Her hair is like a waterfall, full of life.

Vikash Chavda (13)
Soar Valley College

MR STRONG, THE RUGBY PLAYER

He is an enormous red bus,
Loud like thunder on a stormy day,
He is brave as a lion,
As hard as a wardrobe,
As if he goes to the gym everyday!
He'd be 2.00am on a Saturday night,
Like his roaring Ferrari,
He is heavy as metal,
And sour as lemon,
As sour as sour can be,
He has a temper as short as a fuse on a bomb,
As he is destructive as a tornado on the run!

Tariq Kapasi (14)
Soar Valley College

PETER ANDRE - MY IDOL

He's as smooth as velvet,
As posh as a classic car,
Leather seats and a shiny surface,
He's like a sunny day in Ibiza,
He's as cute as a koala,
You'd just want to hug him,
He is like night, black and blue,
You'd want to sit with him under the moonlight,
He's as active as a sporting day,
He'd be 1.00pm on a Saturday afternoon,
In the summertime!

Hinal Sammani (13)
Soar Valley College

WILL SMITH

He is flashy as a sports car
He is fast as a hurricane
As comfortable as a sofa
Big comfy and warm
Sweet as chocolate it will melt in your mouth
As bright as fluorescent flowers
Warm like a sunny day on the beach
He is like a monkey active and cheeky.

Annika Pancholi (13)
Soar Valley College

CREATURES OF THE DEEP

Creatures of the deep who do not sleep.
A life of peace.
Fighting for survival.
Looking for food.
No war or anything.

But people fishing for their lives.
But fish want to stay alive.
A life for a meal.
But that's the way it goes.
We're not the only things you know who
eat things that always grow
Most things do, but only because
they need to.
So enjoy your life.
It's all you've got.
And look after the world it's all we've got
and protect it.

Adam Oates (11)
South Wigston High School

HALLOWE'EN

Hallowe'en comes but once a year,
all the children trick or treat.
Ghosts and ghoulies may appear.
As witches' broomstick down the street.
Fancy dress and apple bobbing.
Horror movies frighten me.
But it's make-believe so there's no sobbing
And I'm having fun, that's plain to see.

As it reaches the witching hour
All the children seek to cower.
As we feel the evil's power
It fills us with dread and fright.
But now it's over another day
And may the next stop be bonfire night.

Ricky Hampson (11)
South Wigston High School

MY FIRST CONCERT

What did you think?
I thought it was bad, your face was gloomy and looked very sad.
What did you think?
Normal I guess, the dance routine was a bit of a mess.
What did you think?
The music great, but the singing was in a bit of a state.
What did you think?
Top notch rate, although the concert started late.
What do I think?
I'm not really sure, I think I'll smile, I won't do a concert at least
for a while.

Paragh Vig (11)
South Wigston High School

The Rude Awakening

Blood flowing like fresh clean water,
Over rocks and wood, into every hole,
Screaming, crying, wanting to be helped,
But all they could do was leave them for dead.

The sky was grey, not a cloud in sight,
Men writing letters to their loved ones,
Not a sound in earshot, not a thing that stirred.
Only the bodies of the day before.

Waking up to the smell of gas,
Invisible to the eye, but choking in the throat,
Trenches were evacuated,
Just as sad soldiers settled for bed.
Gasping for breath, before they drowned.

Boots sinking in mud as soldiers built new trenches,
Picking name tags off people who died,
Defending their country and joining at a young age.

Jade Cross (14)
South Wigston High School

The War

Men shouting and screaming
Running
Dying
And even crying

Running through the mud and guts
Looking at their pals dead
Blood on their faces oh so red
Like an over ripened tomato

Gun strapped across their shoulders
Felt as light as a feather
Mud so thick on their boots
Made them feel like leaded weight

Rotting flesh, alive with maggots
Foul smells attacked your nostrils
The air was filled with fear
Whenever will we get out of here?

Danielle Cooper (13)
South Wigston High School

STAGE FRIGHT!

I love to go to dancing and learn all things new.
Ballet, singing, modern, tap and lots of other things too.
I love to go on the stage, but sometimes my tummy feels tight,
And then I realised that I get stage fright.
I stand backstage all nervous, and my dance going through my mind,
People say you'll be OK and lots being really kind.
Then I hear all people clapping to the girl who's done her dance,
But suddenly I stop and think to myself,
Go on Camilla here's your chance.
The lady stands on the stage and reads my name out loud,
But then I stand onto the stage and see the really big crowd.
I go and get into my position and wait for the music to begin,
I see all people smiling at me but they don't know how I feel within.
The music begins to play and I dance merrily to the song.
I'll just keep on smiling because if I don't I might go wrong.
The judgement time comes, and we all stand in a row,
The adjudicator does her sums, and looks us head to toe.
She placed fourth, third and second and first to number three,
And I stood back in amazement because number three was me!

Camilla Bevans (13)
South Wigston High School

WILDLIFE

As bunnies hop in the fields
And hedgehogs roll up in their shields
The horses are prancing
And the birds are dancing.

Wildlife is a beautiful thing
Such as the lion, the jungle king.
The toads are hopping from lilypad to lilypad
The leopards are rolling around, silly cats, silly cats.

Wildlife is not only creatures,
Flowers, tree and plants it features,
Flowers are colourful and bright,
Trees can grow to a tremendous height.

And deep underground,
Ants are hurrying around,
Digging tunnels for their city,
But from above it does not look pretty.

Spiders have eight legs
In little sacks they keep their eggs,
Guarding their eggs until they hatch,
When their eyes see daylight they despatch

As the sun beats down all around
The air grows warm and dries the ground
The air is like a road for flies
Also for birds in the skies.

About wildlife I hope you remember
It's cold and snowy in December.
So when you're warm and snug indoors
Remember the creatures and their cold paws.

South the birds fly
When winter is nigh
The winds blow high
It's time to say goodbye.

Stacey Sibley (11)
South Wigston High School

DRAGONS

Dragon swooping through the sky,
People watch him flying high,
Screaming children terrified,
Never seen a dragon fly.

Watch him landing like a bird
As all the children spread the word,
Big bulgy eyes,
Long sharp fangs,
As the dragon crawls creepily creaking the cracked land.

Lucy Pole (12)
South Wigston High School

GRENDEL

In the night he prowls around,
waiting to find the perfect victim to slaughter,
roaming about through trees, in hills, through creepy,
cool, monstrous caves, watching Thanes,
picking out just the right one to have for his dinner,
fat ones rather than the slimmer,
He grabs them, rips them, drinks their blood
and then runs off into the dark night leaving the remains,
of that one Thane.

Riah Rupra (11)
South Wigston High School

The Night Stalker

Grendal is the night stalker,
Walks for his food,
Goes through cool caves,
Which are full of mould,
To Heorot Hall,
Where his dinner lies.

Grendal eats his food which is people,
Chomp chomp, crunch crunch away goes the bones of them,
Next goes the blood splat splat on the wall and then the floors.

Grendal leaves the trebble state,
Trailing behind the people blood,
On the stoned path to the sea's edge,
Then this blood trail stopped.

Annika Shawyer (11)
South Wigston High School

War Memories

As the men entered the killing field
Where the poor dying soldiers had keeled

Their uniforms stained red with their brave blood
Nothing there where thousands once stood.

The sound of silence worse than that of gunfire
Dead troops buried up to their shoulders in the quagmire.

Some bodies battered bloody bruised stabbed with knives
All the orphaned kids and desperate widowed wives.

In war nobody really wins and ends up in gladness
Because war only causes death, suffering and sadness.

Lee Bradley (13)
South Wigston High School

JIM JAM

Jim Jam lemon meringue,
Hip hop I forgot,
Swish swish I'm a fish.

Jim Jam here I am
Hip hop I forgot
Tick-tock I'm a clock.

Lewis Byrne (11)
South Wigston High School

3, 2, 1 MILLENNIUM

Line by line of humans
Silent and tranquil
Thinking of a new beginning.

We catch a glimpse
Sliding in thin air
It's the door 10 . . . 9 . . . 8.
A few more seconds to go.

Step by step
Voice by voice 7 . . . 6 . . . 5.
Time is passing (tick-tock, tick-tock)
Wider and wider the door is opening.

People walk through
Where are they?
What is it? 4 . . . 3 . . . 2.

It's a new world
I'm actually here 1 . . . 0 . . . !
In the new millennium.

Kirsty Leanne Rose (13)
The Children's Hospital School

JODIE'S POEM

'Ooh, I love ABBA,' Jodie cried.
'Mama Mia,' Liam tutted, sighed.
'Take me dancing tomorrow night,
I'll wear my skirt - the one's that tight.'

They went dancing the night away,
Boogieing and bopping they did sway
And Liam slipped on a banana skin
And ripped the blouse Jodie was dressed in.

She stamped her feet and shook her head
And screamed at Liam, 'Right you're dead!'
She threw her shandy in his face
And walked away in disgrace.

He went after her and said 'Sorry,'
She said, 'It's OK and not to worry.'
They cuddle and they kissed.
Then they got drunk.

They staggered home at three
Hangovers in their head
Puke by the bed
Lips still numb
Tissue stuck to their bum
A good night on the town
A chance to wear your best gown.

A good night out
A chance to shout
Music to drink
Carrots in the sink
It's hell next day
When you can't find your way home.

Jodie Edwards (15)
The Children's Hospital School